THE
LION
AND THE
GAZELLE

THE MAMMALS
AND BIRDS OF IRAN

Other books by P. N. Humphreys

Practically in the Country (with T. Gabriel), 1988, Comma International Biological Systems.

The Ark Adrift, 1989, Comma International Biological Systems.

Animal Welfare and the Law, 1989, with D. E. Blackman & P. Todd, Cambridge University Press (out of print).

THE
LION
AND THE
GAZELLE

THE MAMMALS
AND BIRDS OF IRAN

P.N. Humphreys
& E. Kahrom

First published in Great Britain 1995 by
Comma International Biological Systems
Lower Coed Morgan,
Nr. Abergavenny, Gwent, U.K.

British Library Cataloguing in Publication Data

A catalogue record for this book is available
from the British Library

ISBN 0 9513977 6 1

Cover Photograph of Gazelle reproduced with
kind permission from Planet Earth

Designed and Produced by Images Publishing (Malvern) Ltd.
Printed and Bound in Great Britain by Bookcraft, Bath, Avon.

Contents

ACKNOWLEDGEMENTS

A book of this nature is not the work of one person, nor even of two. We have been helped at all stages by those who have given freely of their expertise, both in the writing and the eventual production. In the end, we found we had more than enough material, and possibly what had to be left out would have formed another book altogether. The only slightly dark cloud turned out to be the huge increase in copyright fees demanded by the museums, which make it very difficult to publish photographs of some of their treasured possessions without sending the price of the book beyond the means of many readers.

We have not intended to infringe the rights of any author or publishers; if we have, we apologise and would welcome the opportunity to rectify the situation in future editions of the book.

We are grateful to those people in Iran and Great Britain who have provided us with information and photographs and contributed line drawings of birds and animals which are not only extremely decorative, but capture the essential spirit of their subjects. We are grateful to Mike Chapman for imparting his knowledge of camels, to Mrs. Chang of the British Museum and Dr. C. McCarthy of the British Museum (Natural History) for information on snakes and to Eileen Humphreys for her excellent advice on historical matters as well as her permission to make use of one of the maps from her book, *The Royal Road*. Thanks should go to Planet Earth and to Aquila Photographs for kindly allowing us to use photographs from their collections.

Tony Harold, of Images, has backed the concept of the book from the start, and Chris Redman, Catherine Whting and Anita Sherwood have applied their considerable skills to accomplish its birth after a somewhat prolonged pregnancy and not uncomplicated parturition.

To John and Ann
For effecting the Introduction

PREFACE

This book has its origins in a trip made to Iran in 1976 by some of the members of the Royal Society for Asian Affairs. Although the purpose of the tour was to visit the great cities and monuments of the country the extraordinary numbers of birds and other animals that were present everywhere made a deep impression on one of the authors (Patrick Humphreys). This was not necessarily a question of living birds, although numbers were seen and recorded in the published account of the tour (Humphreys, 1977), but rather the artefacts which illustrated animals and birds in a great variety of species and situations in every conceivable historical context. There can be few national cultures more permeated with biology. What is more, the creatures are all portrayed accurately, whether they occur in paintings, pots, stone monuments, carpets, jewellery, or tile work. This means that the biologist can gain an impression of which animals were around hundreds, if not thousands of years ago, and is able to form some view of the climate and ecology of the country at that time. This has proved to be most interesting when considering the status of the Asian Elephant in Persian history.

It was therefore extremely fortuitous that much later both authors found themselves working in the same ecological group in the University of Wales, Cardiff. Dr. Kahrom had worked at a senior level in the Wildlife Department of Iran, and had been responsible for a number of surveys and projects there. He was brought up in Tehran and is therefore ideally placed to knit the past and present aspects of Iranian wildlife together. As readers will see, he is also a talented artist and has kindly allowed some of his beautiful drawings to be included in the illustrations. We have also used our original photographs and a number from museums and other collections to give visual impact to the text.

We have in most cases used the common English names for animals, with their Latin (scientific) names indicated in the first instance. We have arranged the text so as to give a general indication of relationships only, rather than tedious lists of species, sub-species, etc. We have also included common Farsi names by which the various beasts are known. There may be some local or colloquial names which are not known to us, but this seems to happen whenever lists of animal names are compiled. There are said to be over 30 names in English for the smallest pig of the litter! We have also tried to give some indication of the modern condition of the habitats available today.

Dr. Kahrom has visited Iran several times in recent years and has been able bring back information on the existing situation with regard to habitat conservation and environmental awareness. We shall refer to this later, but in general his impression is that the outlook is fairly optimistic and that useful progress is being achieved.

INTRODUCTION

The first introduction to the animals of Persia (or Iran, as it is now known) is often during childhood, when babies learning to crawl are placed for their comfort on a colourful carpet. There are always patterns in a Persian carpet, and many of these incorporate animals and plants. Some will be real pictures, others will be stylised in the extreme, usually depending on where the carpet was made. A little crawler may find himself in close proximity to all sorts of dangerous and bizarre beasts, such as scorpions, tarantulas or camels. Fortunately, mothers of such infants need have no fears; most of the nastier creatures have been woven into the carpet as a sort of good luck charm, to keep away the real ones. Some carpets even have rows of dogs, growling woolenly at strangers. The craftsmen who weave these wonderful textiles like to invest them with reflections of their own lives. The Kash'gai, who live in the mountains of south Persia and who migrate up and down with the seasons, can never stay in one place long enough to grow a decent flower garden for themselves. So they make carpets strewn with bright colours and flower shapes, and thus they can take their gardens with them wherever they go. It appears to be the same with animals. Nomads live very much in intimate contact with their animals and sometimes weave favourite dogs or specially fine camels into their designs as they work, marked perhaps by a stripe of blue or red.

But carpets and rugs are woven by town dwellers as well as nomads; and certain Persian towns and cities are famous for producing carpets of distinctive design, sometimes incorporating materials other than wool, such as silk. Kerman, Nain and Quom are well known in this respect, as are Hamadan and Tabriz. Their carpets are often very large and finely worked, and have received much study by enthusiastic collectors and academics. Those wishing to know more about them in every respect should consult the books on the subject given in the bibliography at the end. The point about them is that a great many are in fact woven pictures, and illustrations of love stories, myths and historical scenes, and can include hunts or pastoral activities among their subjects.

Which brings us to pictures painted on paper or parchment. Originally, the making of books seems to have been confined to that of *The Koran*, for use while travelling and later for permanent reference and education in the mosques. After a while, however, people liked to have copies of some of their favourite stories with them and editions of the most famous ones, such as Firdawsi's *Shahnama* or collections of Saadi's poems, were produced for the rich and famous who could alone give patronage. Such books were made more precious and worthy of the recipient by hand painted illustrations. Thus came about the famous "Persian Miniatures", which have formed yet another area of academic investigation and collectors' acquisitiveness. The astonishing skill of the painters and beauty of what they produced are universally acclaimed; they have left us a record not only of the people and times in which they were painted but a unique historical record of the fauna and flora of the country. From them, too, we can derive a great deal of information and amusement from the representations of various fantastic mythological animals, angels and demons which festoon the pages. The point should be made that the birds and animals in Persian art are often extremely accurately portrayed so that they are recognisable to the zoologists of today; we may have doubts of course about some of the more fantastic creatures; but creatures of flesh and blood like horses, lions, foxes and storks are there doing the things they would do in life (or quite often in death, owing to the popularity of hunting scenes). We shall explore the roles that animals have played in making Persian art the exciting subject that it undoubtedly is and also see if we can learn from it something about the status and distribution of the regional fauna in historical times. According to de Misonne (1968), approximately 129 species of mammals inhabit Iran, and S. Jervis Read (1968) stated that there were about 450 species of birds. These are not very modern texts and doubtless there have been some gains and losses recorded in more recent times; but all the same these are large numbers to be found within one country: Europe, leaving out the Soviet Union, has only about the same numbers of mammals, and for geographical reasons, which we will consider shortly, many more birds are resident in, and migrate through, Iran than is the case with any more ordinary country; but Persia is no "ordinary" country.

Iran as we know it today is three times the size of France and six times the size of the United Kingdom.[1] It is placed between the great land masses of Europe and Asia and between the Russian expanse of steppe and tundra to the north and the arid heat of the Arabian desert and Africa to the south. As has been pointed out many times in the past, the country is a natural crossroads or junction across which migrations of men, animals and even plants have flowed from time immemorial.

Another factor contributing to the multiplicity of species is the existence of two completely different climatic zones. On the northern edge, along the south shore of the Caspian Sea, is a fairly narrow band of extremely wet forested land, rising steeply to the mountains of the

---

[1] Iran's political boundaries have fluctuated considerably over the centuries. We have included items that represent the wider Persian influence including some from what are now very different countries.

Elburz range; to the south of the Elburz the climate is dry to the point of desiccation; deserts, salt pans, blind rivers and sparsely covered mountains are the order of the day. The two biotypes thus created support creatures appropriate to their particular ecology: the famous Caspian Tiger at one time haunted the dense jungle north of the Elburz, while the gazelle, cheetah and onager were more typical animals of the dry central plateau.

This wealth of wildlife was not unobserved by the human inhabitants of the country; their interest was mainly utilitarian: animals were objects which could be pursued and eaten or, in historical times, domesticated. However, it was not long before records of wars, religious activity and even daily life were being carved in stone, or inscribed in seals, jewellery and other artefacts, and animals played an important part. Right from the earliest times the aesthetic gifts of the craftsmen and women who executed this work have been evident; one could rightly suggest that a nation of artists, not at all primitive or crude in their appreciation of space, design and balance, has worked in Iran for more than a thousand years.

The Persians have not always been content to rest complacently in their homeland, they have invaded other countries and been invaded in their turn; thus they have been subject to many outside influences, both from the west and from the east. Greek, Indian and even Chinese arts made their subtle marks, but possibly the most important of these importations has been the one arising from the invasion of the Arabs who brought both their religion and their alphabet with them, and also a style of architecture and decoration which has been, and still is, one of the greatest achievements of Mankind. It might have been a slightly stultifying influence, in that purist and strictly fundamental interpretations of the Islamic religion have been at pains to enforce the Mosaic instruction of "Thou shalt not make any graven image", i.e., representational art was not allowed; only abstracts and calligraphy which could depict the names of God. Calligraphy was not neglected in Persia; there are a great many beautiful examples of this art (even some curious pictures of birds and animals made from calligraphy alone); but it does seem that a rather liberal view was taken, and natural objects, especially flowers and animals, are depicted in vast numbers of post-Arab invasion paintings and decorations. It has been said that the Persians have always had a civilising effect on their conquerors; certainly this is true of the arts.

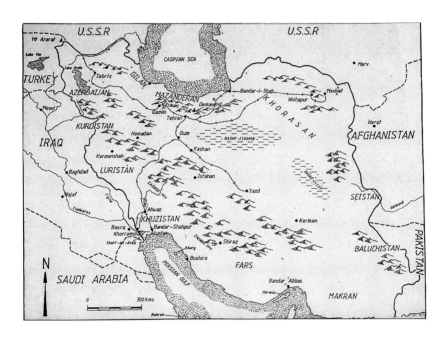

WILDLIFE AND HABITAT CONSERVATION IN IRAN

Iran is a country which grasped the concept of wildlife conservation before it was too late to do anything about it. In 1956 the *Kanoon-e-shekar*, or Hunting Club, was formed, and enacted regulations for the protection of wildlife. At this stage only game species were protected, but in 1957 legal protection was extended to habitats used by the protected animals. The emphasis was on controlling the methods of hunting; close seasons were defined and the killing of certain species was prohibited.

In 1967 Kanoon-e-shekar was expanded and the name changed to the Department of Hunting and Control of Fisheries. Four years later it was felt that the relatively narrow aims and responsibilities of the Department could not control the nation-wide destruction of habitats by industrial development and a new organisation was required with extended and more specialised powers.

The heavy pollution of the towns and cities led to the creation of the Department of the Human Environment, at first a sub-department of the old one, but the responsibilities of both have now been amalgamated into the Department of the Environment (D.E.) which incorporates modern concepts of environmental conservation with its original tasks of protection of wildlife.

The D.E. is responsible for assessing the impacts of different industrial projects on the environment. This enables it to stop or ameliorate projects incompatible with objectives of environmental conservation. Each such project must obtain the approval of the D.E. at its feasibility study stage. The D.E. has a long record of success in this field.

In order to protect the fauna and flora and their habitats the D.E. has established protected areas throughout Iran. These enjoy legal protection at four different levels.

1. NATIONAL PARKS
Park-e-melli

These are vast areas containing resources such as forests, pastures, bodies of water and mountains which represent some of the most outstanding areas of natural beauty. No human activities are allowed in them, and they are designed to preserve a whole natural ecosystem for all future generations. A good example is the Golestan National Park in the north of Iran.

2. NATIONAL NATURAL RESERVES
Assar-e-tabiei-melli

These are outstanding and rare natural phenomena such as ancient trees, and some historical features which need a large protected area surrounding them; for example, the Dehloran National Natural Reserve containing tar springs.

3. PROTECTED AREAS
Mantagheh-e-hefazat-shodeh

These are large areas containing natural resources in which reasonable exploitation is allowed but in such a way that populations of animals and vegetation structure remain sustainable. In these areas 0.2 of the core is designated as a secure zone in which no human activity is allowed. An example is the Kavir Protected Area in Central Iran.

4. WILDLIFE REFUGES
Panahgah-e-hayate-vahsh

These are areas having specific habitats and climatic properties suitable for certain species or groups of wild animals, for example, the Miankaleh Wildlife Refuge.

It is unfortunate that these areas, nicknamed *Gols* (flowers) by the environmentalists, which had been well protected since their establishment, were invaded by local people during and just after the Revolution. The sheer numbers of trespassers, uncontrolled hunting and shooting, and grazing and tree-felling caused them serious damage.

Today, there are about 80 different areas covering about 8 million hectares which are protected by the game guards of the D.E. The size of these areas varies from about 0.5 hectares to 1,295,400 hectares. As well as this, five rivers provide habitats for aquatic animals.

The long-term plan of the D.E. is to provide facilities for people to use these areas in a controlled manner. The government also encourages sustainable and environmentally-sound tourism, and is in contact with similar organisations around the world. New ideas are passed to Iranian scientists who tailor them to Persian conditions and ways of life. A greatly increased number of ecological courses in the Universities has been incorporated in the engineering and technical curriculum and environmental issues are once again "fashionable" in Iran.

While the D.E. is preparing its staff to take up new challenges, the old duties have not been neglected. Protection of wildlife, regulation of hunting and angling and habitat protection remain. Endangered species are being recognised and measures taken to protect them. Some of the projects have aroused international interest; among them the Siberian White Crane Project, the Houbara Bustard Project, and the search for the Persian Tiger and formidable Cheetah.

As part of the international efforts to find solutions to environmental problems the Iranians have realised the importance their own contributions can make to the global environmental scene, and together with the incorporation of local ancient knowledge with modern scientific concepts, the future of wildlife and habitat protection seems secure in Iran.

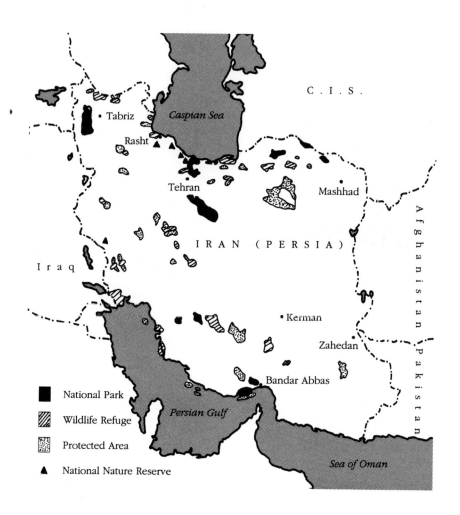

C . I . S .

Tabriz

Caspian Sea

Rasht

Tehran

Mashhad

I R A N (P E R S I A)

Iraq

Kerman

Zahedan

Bandar Abbas

Persian Gulf

Sea of Oman

Afghanistan Pakistan

National Park
Wildlife Refuge
Protected Area
National Nature Reserve

PART ONE

MAMMALS

HORSES AND ASSES

(Family: *Equidae*)

HORSE
(*Equus;* Persian: *Asb)*

The origin of the horse is undoubtedly Asia..Vast flat spaces, alternately baked and frozen, seem destined to have evolved a mammal that was hardy and able to travel widely; that could subsist on dry and semi desert plants; and had a hard foot impervious to stony ground, combined with a turn of speed that could give it some protection from predators.

A number of horses and horse-like animals such as PRZEVALSKI'S HORSE (*Equus caballus Przevalski*), the ONAGER (*Equus hemionus*) and DONKEY *(Equus asinus)* have made their appearance on the steppes and deserts of Asia, although the absolute divisions between them and the common names used by nineteenth century explorers are not always clear to the modern reader of old texts. However, in Persian art the horse is clearly illustrated in all its forms – war-horse, elegant hack, or common domestic donkey – so that there can be no doubt in the observer's mind. Quite often, the animal is an indicator of the social class of its owner or rider: the hero or prince has a handsome horse; his vizier is mounted on a mule; while peasants and the like have to make do with the humble donkey. Curiously, the Ancient Egyptians never portrayed horses in their decorated tableaux until they had established contact with the Persians; after that, pictures of horses were frequent.

The Persians had a tremendous reputation for horse-breeding in the Ancient World and some of the civilisations with which they co-existed, such as the Parthians, developed the art of warfare on horseback to an extremely fine pitch. The famous "Parthian Shot" involved fleeing from the enemy and suddenly turning in the saddle at full gallop and letting loose a volley of well directed arrows. The feigned retreats of the Parthians often led into traps; lured on by the fleeing light horse, the enemy would suddenly find himself confronted by a battalion or two of heavy horse, armoured and equipped with spears and lances, while the formerly fleeing archers on the wings closed behind them[2].

Sanatruq, a Parthian King, c. 370 A.D.

Photo: P. N. Humphreys

---

[2] Although the "Parthian Shot" is generally ascribed to the Parthians who were adept at its use, the tactic was in fact used long before their time. Xenophon describes it being employed by the Persians in his account of the campaign on behalf of Cyrus, the son of Darius, against his brother.

Many of the nomadic tribes such as the Kashg'ai and Lurs still pride themselves on their mastery of the art of shooting from the saddle; nowadays, however, they use guns. Shooting partridges as they rise, while hurtling over the stones of a mountain on horseback, is an accomplishment attained by few of our western sportsmen.

Much of what we know of horses in ancient times is derived from the reliefs of hunting and battle scenes which were means of recording interesting and significant events many centuries before books and newspapers were invented. Those blood-thirsty forerunners of the Persians, the Assyrians, were particularly keen on this kind of record and there are some magnificent examples of the art in the various western museums, notably the British Museum in London. Running horses, indeed running animals of all sorts, were always portrayed with their legs in maximum extension, as if they were flying, with all feet off the ground. We know now, from cinematography, that this position is never attained in life; even at full gallop the only time all four feet are off the ground is as the stride is started. The convention of depicting galloping animals in this way lasted until late into the nineteenth century, as in the favourite Victorian pictures of English foxhunting, with the squire and parson sailing over the hedges, sometimes to land upside down in a muddy ditch.

Throughout Persian history, the horse was treated as a steed or baggage carrier and not a means of traction, except for the very light two-wheeled chariots that were used where ground conditions made it possible; this was of course because the horse-collar was not invented until late medieval times (in Europe). For serious traction, such as ploughing, oxen were always preferred. Just occasionally teams of mules seem to have been employed to pull wagons containing provisions or extra amunition or even parties of people; however, this meant the sacrifice of mobility to some extent, and in most of the ancient wars mobility was all important. The Romans, used to large, well disciplined armies, with walls of armoured troops and baggage trains in close attendance and a carefully worked out plan of battle, learned their lesson the hard way when they came up against the Parthians at the battle of Carrhae, 60 B.C. The usual Parthian tactics led to a dreadful defeat for the Romans, whose commander Crassus sent his son Publius off to chase the retreating Parthians, only to meet them coming back a little later with his son's head raised triumphantly on a lance.

The Persians themselves have always been proud of the quality of their horses and the superiority of their horse-breeders. Darius I, in one of his inscriptions, refers to his country as a "land of fine horses and good men". In fact, so much was the horse revered, that its name, *asb*, was incorporated into royal titles; for example, Tarmasb, Garshasb, Hazarasb, Lohrasb, Goshtasb, Arzasb, Jamasb, Gordanasb and so on. There are 80 different names for horses in the Persian language; one of them being *chougan*, the polo-pony[3]. Omar Khayam named 43 of them, each with its special characteristics. The Arabic language uses *fars* for a horse and its rider, the same name as the country of Persia. Certain breeds of horses were particularly prized as cavalry chargers. Herodotus speaks of the Nisaean horses being used in the battle of Thermopylae (493 B.C.). These were very large animals originating from the great Nisaean Plain in Media, where they were also used to draw the King's chariot. Earlier, the Assyrians used stallions extensively in their military campaigns – Sargon II was contemptuous of an enemy who escaped from a battle riding a mare. At that time, the Uratu, living in what is now northern Turkey, were considered the best trainers of military horses. Breeds such as the Kusian and Mesian were

---

[3] See Appendix 1: A History of Polo in Iran.

recognised, white horses were greatly prized, and in fact were often dedicated to certain Gods and associated temples for ceremonial purpose. This tradition is still observed in the Middle East: one has only to see the film of Saddam Hussein's victory parade! There is a nice, if possibly apocryphal, story of a horse being used to decide a royal succession. It is said that when Darius I and his brothers were disputing the succession after the death of their father it was settled on the question of whose horse would neigh first of all in the morning. Darius arranged for his groom to introduce his stallion to a breeding mare in the evening, so that when he took the animal back to the same spot at the crack of dawn it would become excited at the prospect and start neighing. One feels the Gods were guided along the right path just a little at times.

The great reliance on the horse in military campaigns led to all sorts of logistical difficulties when it came to supplying fodder. When Sennacherib (704-681 B.C.) decided to attack the Elamites in south-west Persia he arranged for stores of grain and straw to go by ship, although presumably the horses themselves went overland most of the way. The care of horses seems hardly to have changed over the centuries. A broken Hittite text used by the Assyrians speaks of letting the horses roll after unharnessing, to be followed by a rub down and foddering (Saggs, 1984).

Much of what we know about animals in those remote times we have learned from carvings and inscriptions on stones and rock faces. The impressive friezes of men and animals bearing tribute to the Great King at Persepolis seem to have been executed by men with at least two schools of artistic tradition behind them. The Royal horses from Punt and Armenia differ considerably in execution from the Scythian horses. This also applies to some of the other animals depicted (Olmstead, 1948).

Shapur I (r) is invested as King by the God Ahura Mazda (l).   P. N. Humphreys

Shapur river gorge, the site of inscriptions on rock face.   P. N. Humphreys

As times changed so did the type of horse we see illustrated. We pass from the sturdy and powerful cavalry chargers of the Sassanian rulers, to the elegant riding horses painted with such loving care by the artists of Safavid times; to the rough, tough ponies of the steppes that played such a part in the devastating invasions by the Mongols under Genghis Khan and Timur the Lame (Tamberlane). These Mongols were horsemen of the highest calibre, some of them spending almost all of their waking hours in the saddle. Their Shamanistic religion is thought to have involved horse sacrifice, and they perfected an efficient postal service using relays of horses between staging posts across the vast plains of Central Asia. An urgent message could be carried 200 miles a day.

The Mongols used mares' milk as a beverage and fermented it to make an alcoholic drink, *qumis*, as well as cheese which they hardened in the sun and used as "hard" rations when travelling. Every year each clan undertook a hunt of antelopes, gazelle, etc., to make sure of a supply of meat for the winter; these manoeuvres served as training excursions against neighbouring tribes or larger nations. On campaign, they were organised on a decimal system, with 1,000 and 10,000 units of horsemen, each soldier usually taking up to five horses with him. Because their horses were so small and hardy their armies were not encumbered with baggage trains and the need to provide hay or corn, but were prepared to live on the country they conquered and then move on, having massacred the populations and laid waste the countryside. In this way they attained great mobility and with it an element of surprise. Flocks and herds followed on behind, being replenished by animals stolen from conquered territories. Sometimes, this sort of behaviour led them into difficulties, as when Hulagu complained in a letter to the Roman emperor of his difficulty in finding fodder after the capture of Damascus; but Syria was still a more or less forested country in those days and unsuitable for large numbers of horses, so it is not surprising. Not infrequently they would return to a city they had ransacked a few weeks previously and massacre any survivors that had escaped the first time. In this way they raged and looted their way across Asia and Europe even to the gates of Vienna, before rushing back to Mongolia to settle the succession when one of the great Khans died, as happened in 1241, when Ogedu expired. After this, in fact, they never returned in full force, nor had a lasting influence on the peoples they conquered. Possibly the only folk memory now existing of the Mongolian incursions is the fear and dread they inspired in the peoples of places like the Ukraine and the Balkans, It seems certain that they substantially reduced the populations of those that resisted them and that some of those took many years to recover (Morgan, 1986; Lambton, 1988).

Apart from the famous breeds of horse developed in Persia over the ages there were also some well known individuals, both real and mythical. Perhaps the most remarkable is Raksh, the steed belonging to the great hero and Super-man Rustum, whose deeds are related in the *Shahnama*. Raksh was himself a Super-horse: he could fly, he could out-run a gazelle and he could communicate with his master. He was also extremely ferocious and killed three of the thieves who came to steal him on one occasion. He had remarkable eyesight and it was said that he could see an ant's footprints on a dark cloth at two leagues distance. Needless to say he was well known in the circles within which Rustum moved and it was impossible to hide him; after the theft he was soon found and restored to his owner. He is shown in numerous Persian miniatures engaged in valiant deeds such as lion hunts and dismembering divs (demons).

A horse head cast in silver from the 4th century AD. The technique of applying silver ornamentations to silver objects was a speciality of the Iranians. Photo: E. Kahrom

Other heroes and heroines owned famous horses. Shirin, the great beauty of the romantic tale of Kosraw and Shirin, travelled over the dusty plain on her jet-black steed, Shibdaz, hoping to meet Kosraw. He, who was travelling the other way, hoping to meet her, saw her fine horse tethered in a grove surrounding a fresh-water pool in which the lady was having a bath. Rather than embarrass her, Kosraw travelled on without introducing himself, and thus the lovers did not meet until much later. This scene is also a favourite miniature.

A real horse was Bucephalus, the war-horse of Alexander the Great. The name implies "Bull-headed" so that Bucephalus was probably a weight-bearing military charger, thick in limb and stout in build. He carried Alexander throughout his Persian campaign and only died after being wounded in the battle against Porus and his elephants.

31

Alexander conducted a proper funeral service for his old friend, and proposed to dedicate a town in his name, although its precise location has never been properly ascertained. Commemorative coins and medals illustrating the last hours of Bucephalus are still in existence.

In 680, the Imam Hussein, revered founder of the Shia sect of Islam, rode out on his horse, "Zol-Zanah", with 72 companions to face a vastly superior force of enemies at Kerbela (now in Iraq). The little band, including Hussein's two young sons, was cut to pieces, and he himself was finally slaughtered after a brave resistance. Zol-Zanah fled back to the encampment where he and his master had spent the night, and when Hussein's family saw the riderless horse they knew the worst had happened. This scene has been the source of many miniatures and poems in Iran. The episode is commemorated every year in Iran in the ceremony of *Muharram*, when religious zealots march the streets, lashing themselves to simulate the martyrdom.

That close relative of the horse, the *Wild Ass* or *Onager*, has figured in Persian art down the ages as a favourite and prestigious quarry for the huntsman. Not only were they extremely wary animals but had a tremendous turn of speed and endurance, so that a horseman could not expect to be able to ride them down in straight pursuit, but needed to distract or turn them in some way, as for instance by chasing a foal, hoping that the dam would also be diverted and come within range of arrows or hounds.

> They say the lion and the lizard keep
> The courts where Jamshyd gloried and drank deep;
> And Bahram[4], that great hunter,

---

[4] Bahram was also known as Bahram-gur, *gur* denoting Wild Ass in Persian. *Gur* is also Persian for grave, so that the original poem has special connotations.

The Wild Ass stamps o'er his head
And he lies fast asleep.

(The Rubaiyat of Omar Khayam, trs. Fitzgerald.)

The great number of representations of onagers being hunted in Persian and Middle Eastern Art should not blind us to the fact that in very early times they seem to have been, at least partly, domesticated and used to pull carts and chariots. This is confirmed by Epstein (1984) who describes a Sumerian cylinder seal of c. 2060 B.C. showing the chariot of a city god drawn by four onagers. The same author states a list pertaining to the royal stables at Ur of a slightly later date and refers to 78 teams, each of four onagers. Onagers seem to have been used to pull war chariots by certain military groups until early Christian times and Herodotus speaks of onager-chariots in Xerxes army (480 B.C.). Strabo knew of chariots drawn by onagers in Iran in 21 A.D.

The harnessing of such a wild and speedy animal must have provided an exciting ride, to say the least. It is not at all clear whether these onagers were truly domesticated or merely captured from the wild and tamed, which is apparently easy to achieve. That they were used for food as well is clear by the quantities of bones found with those of other domestic animals throughout the region.

Although very much less common than in previous times, there are still onagers in Iran. There seem to be at least two populations, one located in the central Kavir and another more southerly in the area around Shiraz. Numbers are not known for certain, but this is not surprising as the onager is notorious for vanishing into the heat haze of its desert habitat, its colouration and markings being the perfect camouflage. According to a survey carried out in 1975 by the Iranian Department of the Environment, the largest groups were found in the Kavir National Park and Bahram-e-Gur Protected Area. Other small groups were located in the Tooran Protected Area and near Kerman. The animal mostly lives in family groups comprising a stallion, several females and a group of young and immatures. Sometimes two or more groups join up and occasionally more than a hundred can be present together. Although most onagers in Iran live within Protected Areas or National Parks, precise numbers are not known. The largest group in the Bahram-e-Gur Protected Area consisted of 70 individuals.

ASS
(Equus asinus; Persian: *Xaer)*

The domestic donkey is found not only in Iran, but throughout the Middle East and the Mediterranean countries of Europe. Early evidence of the regard in which the donkey was held has been shown by the discovery of a temple or shrine devoted to the God Shakkran dated about 2250 B.C. at Tell Brak, in eastern Syria. This God was generally supposed to protect animals such as the gazelle, wild sheep and onager which lived on the steppe, and it is suggested that the temple was situated at an important caravanserai which served the trade routes into Anatolia and beyond. Evidently the domestic relatives of the wild animals were also included in Shakkran's sphere of influence (*The Times*, 24th March, 1993).

The ass appears to have been of African origin and first domesticated by the Egyptians. There are a number of variations in size and colour. Not strong enough to play much of a part as a draught animal, it is used almost entirely as a pack or riding animal. The ass is still a valuable beast of burden for the small farmer or nomad; its dietary requirements are not difficult to satisfy, as it will eat almost any vegetation including dry and spiny plants typical of desert regions. It can endure thirst, though not as well as the camel, and normally can manage to put in about thirty years of hard labour in its lifetime. It is also extremely sure-footed, and has been much used in the great caravans that crossed the mountainous areas of Asia. Ass's milk had a great reputation for its cosmetic qualities, and Cleopatra and other fabled beauties of the ancient world are said to have bathed in it. Like goat's milk in Europe, ass's milk was used extensively for feeding children.

The donkey, as the poor man's animal, has not figured very prominently in Persian art. It appears in a few illustrations of fables, usually in a rather derisory capacity, often being shown as thin and wretched in contrast to the beautiful steeds of the princes or nobles who are the subjects of the picture. This is not really surprising, as poor donkey owners were not likely to be collectors of fine art, whereas there was always the possibility of patronage with princes.

In spite of this the donkey has always been a familiar animal to Iranians, and apart from the centres of big cities, donkeys are to be found nearly everywhere. Perhaps because of its general humbleness the ass has been the preferred mode of transport for mullahs and those of religious persuasion, including the Prophet Mohammed himself. Moglessi, a leading Islamic historian, in his much publicised book *Holiattol Motiaghin* (Ornament of the Faithful), still revered by Shias in Iran, has recounted many *Hadiths* (traditional discourses) of the Prophet and his successors (the Imams) which deal with donkeys. Included in the book is a chapter on the general care of donkeys. In one of the *Hadiths* Mohammed enjoins his followers to feed their donkeys before themselves; and in conjunction with this the 6th Imam suggests that a buyer of a donkey will have its costs, i.e. food, provided by God.

There are many allusions to asses in Persian literature and

35

proverb. The much loved tales of the Mullah Nasreddin contain many donkey anecdotes, including the following: A man went to the Mullah's house to borrow his donkey. The Mullah answered the door and said, "I'm sorry, I've already lent him to somebody else." At that moment the donkey brayed within the house. The borrower said, "But I can hear your donkey, he must be at home!" The Mullah shouted, "Who do you trust, the donkey or me!"

A traditional proverb says that "Giving advice to a stupid man is like reciting the Koran to a donkey". Another makes the analogy: "He's stuck like an ass in mud", (meaning, his problems are almost insuperable).

The great poet Saadi tells the tale of a man who spent many days trying to teach his donkey to speak. A wise man watched him for some time and finally said, "Your ass will not learn to speak from you; why don't you learn silence from him?"

These, and many other pieces of proverbial wisdom, underline the alleged stupidity of the donkey as against the even greater stupidity of Mankind in general. Thus, lowly as he is, the ass can still be an object lesson for the man in the street.

CAMELS

(Family: *Camelidae*)

The ONE-HUMPED DROMEDARY (*Camelus dromedarius*; Persian: *Sotor yek koaneh*) and the TWO-HUMPED BACTRIAN (*Camelus bactrianus*; Persian: *Sotor do kohaneh*) have played an important part in the economy of historical Iran. Neither can be said to be indigenous to the country, the dromedary having arrived from Arabia and Africa in the south and the bactrian having been introduced from the steppes of Central Asia. Both are well illustrated in the great frieze of men and animals at Persepolis, thus showing the extensive foreign influence enjoyed by the Kings of Persia at that time.

It has been said, somewhat unkindly, that "the camel is an animal designed by a committee". It is true, though, that camels have some unique physiological features that have made them the useful animals they are in an arid environment. Chapman (1991) gives a good account of their evolutionary development and peculiar biological characteristics. The *Camelidae*, in fact, were an evolutionary product of north America. One branch of the order, *Tylopoda*, migrated south and gave rise to the llamas, guanacos, vicunas and alpacas; while the true camels seem to have drifted across what is now the Bering Strait into Asia and north Africa. The differences between the two species are perhaps less than they appear; they have the same number of chromosomes and hybridise easily and successfully, and both are two-humped during embryonic development. Nevertheless, some important distinctions remain. As Chapman points out, the single hump of the dromedary is better adapted to the hotter climates of Africa and Arabia; it has a smaller surface area and when the fat reserves of which it consists are depleted it just shrinks in size, unlike the humps of the bactrian which flop over to either side. For some reason too, the milk of the dromedary will not make a good curd and therefore cannot be made into cheese; whereas owners of bactrians preserve an important quantity of their camels' milk which forms a hard, long-keeping cheese, useful to take as food on journeys across the steppes or desert.

The capacity of camels to go for days without food or water is due to their extreme efficiency at extracting nourishment from the unpromising forage available to them for much of the year, storing it (in the form of fat tissue in the humps) and the equally efficient concentration of urine which they achieve in their kidneys. Camels are the ultimate exploiters of good times and bad – when rains have fallen and pasture is green and plentiful they eat well and put on fat in their humps; in dry, hard periods they exist on their reserves and wait for better fortune. Their large, padded feet are ideal for travelling across the shifting sands of the desert; their size and stride enables them to progress at a steady walking pace for long periods bearing a useful amount of weight. Not without good reason have they been called the "ships of the desert".

According to Mason (1984) camels were rare in the countries of Syria, Palestine and Mesopotamia until the Aramaean invasions from Central Arabia between the 16th and 13th Centuries B.C. The first great invasion of camel nomads was that of the Ishmaelites (Midianites) c. 1100 B.C. As the status of these rough warriors improved over time, so it was seen that the camel could be used for commerce. Gradually its use increased, so much so in fact that the use of the wheel was practically abandoned in the areas between Afganistan and Morocco in the period 300-600 A.D. The spread of Islam, following the birth and teaching of the Prophet Mohamed, would have made much slower progress than it did without the camels' employment in the communication systems of the time.

Thus, we find few very early depictions of camels in Persian art. They were known, it is true, but it seems that only since about 300 A.D. were they really familiar domestic animals. In general, it seems, they were kept out of cities. Not only are they large, smelly and slightly dangerous animals to be mingling with the crowds in narrow streets and alleys, but their owners and drivers have always had a slightly unsavoury reputation themselves, being people "of no fixed abode", wandering freely in the world under the stars and not really the sort of folk suitable to be received in the lush and scented apartments of the ruling classes. Camels therefore assembled outside the city gates, and the caravans were organised so as to have fodder and water available at the start and ends of their journeys. The animals were actually physically prevented from entering the city by the low gateway; the famous "eye of the needle". The drivers could come and go and solicit business in the bazaars and caravanserais within, the merchandise being taken through the camel gate on the backs of men or donkeys. A fine example of an ancient camel gate is seen on the outside wall of the Parthian city of Hatra, where there is a relief of a male and female camel, the female suckling a calf.

The Camel Gate at Hatra.   Photo: P. N. Humphreys

Dromedary.   Photo: M. J. Chapman

The frustrations and delays encountered so often in a modern airport are as nothing compared with the departure of a camel caravan. The last-minute bargaining with travellers, the sudden discovery of unsuitable camels among those already hired, the total absence of essential drivers or guides, usually suspected of being drunk, assassinated or in prison, a new consignment of baggage hitherto unheard of and rumours of bandits at every stopping place along the way, all conspired to delay departure until it was too late to start that day. When, finally, the complaining and roaring animals had been loaded up and the caravan set off, it was often to travel only a few miles out of town, when camp was made for the night. This was so that if anything had been forgotten or yet more changes needed to be made, it would be possible to arrange the following morning. In the summer, caravans travelled by night anyway, and the eerie, soft sound of a caravan passing by almost invisibly in the dark has been described by several European travellers in the east (Burton, 1855; Doughty, 1908; Welland, 1977).

Camels have been used in warfare over the ages with only moderate success. Occasionally battles with camels involved have caused panic among the horses on the opposing side, as horses have to become accustomed to camels before they tolerate their presence. But the mobility and quiet approach of a contingent of lightly armed camel riders could no doubt confer advantages to desert raiders. The hosts of Midian, referred to earlier, seem to have been a large tribe of desert nomads temporarily displaced northwards by drought in their own grazing grounds, and not an organised conquering army, though doubtless they caused sore tribulation to the local Hebrews trying to settle down to agriculture in Palestine, as nomads do everywhere to sedentary farmers.

The Persian hero, Bahram-Gur, is portrayed in the *Shahnama*, and subsequently pictorially, as using his racing camel to go hunting gazelle. Moreover, on one occasion he took along a lady friend, one Azadeh, who livened up the proceedings by strumming on her lyre as they rode along. The expedition ended in disaster, as she was foolish enough to criticise his shooting, whereupon he threw her off the camel. Later on, Assassin Kings were portrayed as performing the Bahram-Gur camel-borne feats of venery (Ettinghausen, 1979).

The European belief that the camel was a committee-designed animal has been taken a step further by the Persians. In the fable of Majnoon and Leila, after the love lorn Majnoon had communed with the animals in the wilderness, they felt that as he had no transport he would be unable to make much impression on the young lady; so each animal volunteered to donate a part of his body to form a suitable steed: the result was a camel. "Majnoon's Camel" is used today when referring to a hotch-potch of disparate and ill-considered ideas.

41

Bahram-Gur and Azadeh go hunting gazelle.   Photo: E. Kahrom

There are few camels in Iran today. In a table of world camel populations Mason (1984) notes a decline in Iranian camels from 0.60 million in 1948/52, to 0.03 million in 1981; there are probably fewer still today. The only camels sighted during a journey in 1976 were some two dozen dromedaries being grazed not far from Kerman. They were described as being used in the smuggling business; having been forced to swallow a packet of contraband (possibly drugs) on the coast of the Persian Gulf or Baluchistan, they were driven inland by little known tracks at night and eventually slaughtered in a safe spot and the contraband removed. A sad fate for the formerly esteemed kings of the desert!

SHEEP

(Ovis aries; Persian: Gusfaend)

Iran is probably the epicentre of the sheep. The wild varieties which still exist seem to have evolved to exploit the dry and mountainous terrain which constitutes so much of the land mass of Asia; much of it inhospitable and very cold in winter while arid and hot in the summer. There is some debate about the true division of the wild species, a few of which, although having differing chromosome counts, interbreed successfully with each other and with domestic sheep. Wild sheep seem to have been a frequent victim of the hunters of ancient times, and the variety known as M A R C O   P O L O ' S   S H E E P *(Ovis poli)*, which lives far to the east of Iran, has been the target of European big-game hunters endeavouring to bag a head with its magnificent spread of horns as a trophy.

The wild sheep which gave rise to the domestic races are probably the M O U F L O N *(Ovis orientalis)* and the A R G A L I *(Ovis ammon)* together with the U R I A L *(Ovis vignei)*. It is difficult to say how much each contributed to the domestic animal, and how soon the value of the underlying wool beneath the hair coats of the wild sheep were appreciated and bred for. There is some evidence that sheep were at least partly domesticated in the region as early as 9000 B.C. from deposits of bones, of which a large proportion were from juvenile animals. The early Sumerians kept sheep, for milk, and illustrated them on cylinder seals and similar artefacts. They also used the wool, but felted it for their dress-coats with pointed hemlines which seem to have been the normal garments of the period. Some of their sheep had corkscrew horns, and some of the ewes were hornless. Not all of them seem to have had woollen fleeces; some were more hairy like their wild ancestors. Other sorts seem to have had wool, coiled horns and a thin tail. Yet a third type seems to have had similar horns, but no fleece and a fat tail. (Ryder, 1984). It may be, of course, that we are misinterpreting some of the pictures we see of sheep of that time, in that some of them would have been shorn, and some not. The iron sheep shears was invented in Europe about 1000 B.C., until then sheep were plucked or combed with the assistance of a stone or copper hand blade.

Sheep have appeared in the regional art ever since, reflecting their economic importance. The Biblical patriarchs were nomadic chieftains with a great many sheep and goats to their names, and the story of Jacob and Leah shows that some of them were fairly sophisticated geneticists. There is a fine depiction of sheep with curved horns, Roman noses, fat tails and full fleeces among the tributes being brought to Darius on the processional frieze at Persepolis. These are possibly of Assyrian origin. Wool was a very important crop in ancient times, particularly in Babylonia, only corn and oil being equal.

The FAT-TAILED SHEEP which predominate in the region usually have coarse-fibred fleeces, and are therefore particularly suited to provide wool for carpets. The great demand for Persian carpets world-wide has led to a relative shortage of carpet wool, and a wool-dyer at Kashan in 1976 was bemoaning the fact that the importation of Merino wool from New Zealand was leading to the production of

Domestic rams, part of tribute procession at Persepolis.   Photo: P. N. Humpreys

production of softer, poorly wearing carpets of inferior quality. A peculiar sheep product is the famous "Persian Lamb" pelt, used in the fur trade. This is in fact the skin of new-born lambs from certain breeds which have a tight and curly fleece. "Persian" is probably a misnomer in this context, as these sheep originally came from the Karakul region of Central Asia: possibly the pelts were exported through Persia. Today, the main centre of production is south Africa. Sheep milk is used in Iran for the production of yoghurt, cheese, ice-cream, and the yoghurt-soda mixture, *doogh*, a common and refreshing beverage. A miniature painting, attributed to Mir Sayyid 'Ali (c. 1540) shows a nomadic encampment with various domestic scenes. In one corner an old woman is milking a nanny-goat into a handsome pot, there are several ewes and lambs with them, while the shepherd is serenading the little flock with music from his long pipe. Another man is spinning a thread. (Welch, S. C., 1976).

Sheep in Iran today are still kept under a system of transhumance, in which the flocks are taken to mountain pastures in the spring, to return to lower ground in the winter. The tribal people who own these sheep have a remarkable rapport with them; often lambs may be born on migration, and it is not uncommon to see these little creatures sitting in front of a rider of a horse or camel, to be handed back to their mother's care when the time comes to encamp for the night. Sheep are used for meat as well as wool, and it was the custom among some tribes to sacrifice a sheep in the path of a guest to demonstrate that he was welcome and a good meal would be forthcoming shortly.

While in camp, the women of the tribes set up their portable looms and proceed with the work of weaving carpets. These are made in traditional patterns and may reflect the joining of two clans in a marriage, or the birth of a son to a chief or other event. They are passed down from generation to generation as heirlooms. Others are sold commercially in such cities as Shiraz and may be an important part of the income of the clan – even a fairly modest rug can fetch over a thousand pounds and a larger carpet a great deal more. It is a mistake to think that because these tribes lead a rather hard and difficult life in physical terms they are impoverished materially; this is not so, and many are in fact very well off, and own businesses and property in the cities as well as flocks and herds. Many have contributed greatly to Iranian political and cultural life. It is interesting to contemplate how much of both Iranian and British civilisation, in terms of cultural monuments and other artefacts, can be traced to the backs of a humble ruminant. The riches derived from the carpet trade and the prosperity of the wool and cloth merchants in medieval times in England have given both countries an architectural inheritance unsurpassed in the rest of the world.

WILD SHEEP

There are three sub-species of wild sheep which live in the northern mountainous parts of Iran and another inhabits the southern mountains of Fars and Kerman:

The U R I A L *(Ovis ammon;* Persian: *Gouch-e-urial)* is found in the north east of the country. Unlike the ibex, the Urial prefers the undulating hills characteristic of this region, rather than the rocky peaks. This sheep is an excellent runner but not a very good climber, and is one of the most beautiful varieties of the region. The body is large and powerful, measuring up to 1 metre in height and weighing up to 85 kilogrammes, with even bigger males occasionally found; the females are smaller. The spectacular horns of the rams are often an indication of territorial success, as the sheer size of them may serve to intimidate rivals.

The W E S T E R N   R E D   S H E E P *(Ovis ammon gmelini;* Persian: *Ghouch-e-Armani)* inhabits parts of Turkey, Armenia and Russia as well as the north-west mountains of Iran.

The main difference between the Western Red Sheep and the other sheep lies in the configuration of the horns. In this animal they have a rounded base and turn around the head so that in some cases they meet at the back of the neck. The females are much smaller than the males in this sub-species, with only small horns. Commonly met with in Rezaieh Province, large numbers were introduced onto Kabudan Island in Lake Rezaieh about two hundred years ago. This is the largest island in the lake, although its total area is only 33 square kilometers. The sheep found the island much to their liking and increased rapidly to about 3,000, by which time they had grazed out the vegetation and two thirds of them starved to death one winter. In order to control the population leopards were introduced and since then the population has remained at a more sustainable 1,000 animals.

Wild sheep   Photo: E. Kahrom

The E L B O R Z   R E D   S H E E P *(Ovis ammon orientalis)* is the typical sheep of the Central Elborz, and is what the people of Tehran might see if they drive out of the city towards the north. These sheep are half-way in conformation between the Urial and the Western Red Sheep and horns have characteristics of both species, opening outwards like those of the Western Red Sheep and then turning down like those of the Urial.

The LURISTAN SHEEP *(Ovis ammon Luristan)* inhabits the mountainous area of Luristan, in the south of the Province of Fars. Here, the summers are dry and hot and winters are mild and wet. There are some shrubs, but forest typical of dry lands is prevalent. Mature lotus trees can be found in the valleys and cedar (juniper) grows on the highest peaks. Between them, wild pistachio and almond trees are common. In this area is found a wild sheep that is smaller than all the other sub-species. In the southern parts of Luristan, the increased heat influences the body size in a negative way, so that some of the smallest sheep in the world are found here.

As with the ibex, the horns of these beautiful sheep have inspired artists and craftsmen throughout history, and exaggerated horn shapes have been used for rhytons and other artefacts by the Achaeminids and other dynasties.

Wild Sheep   Illustration: E. Kahrom

GOATS

(Capra hircus)

There is some evidence that goats were domesticated even earlier than sheep. According to Bokonyi (1976) remains of domestic goats were found on the Iranian plateau, dated about 8000 B.C. The wild goat is the immediate ancestor of the domestic animal. It is also called the Bezoar, which is a corruption of the Persian *apad-zahr*, meaning antidote to poison. The antedote is taken from the bezoar stone, a calculus found sometimes in the stomach of the goat (and other ruminants) and long believed to be an effective remedy against various poisons. The Persian word for mountain goat is in fact *pazan* (Mason, 1976).

The wild goat itself is a very impressive animal, the males possessing long scimitar or sabre-shaped horns, and a handsome beard. The females have shorter horns. Additionally, all goats possess scent glands under the tail, much pronounced in the males. The coat is generally hairy, although some of the domestic breeds such as the *Angora* (Ankhara, Turkey) have a fine coat (mohair) and the *Cashmere* goats (also known as Pashmina goats, from the Persian *pashm* = wool) have a hairy outer coat with a very fine woolly undercoat.

There are other differences between sheep and goats. Goats are essentially browsing animals, being partial to shrubs and trees as well as grass for their forage; indeed they have been blamed for the creation of deserts because of their sheer will to survive and ability to tackle almost any vegetation, however dry or thorny. In general, goats are even more suited to mountainous country than sheep. The males fight

50

differently, too; sheep like to step back some paces and then charge, head to head, relying on the fortified construction of their foreheads to stun the opponent, or at least give him a nasty headache. Goats on the other hand use their horns much more to first intimidate and finally to wound a rival. Goats carry their tails upright, while those of sheep are pendulous. The two species are totally distinct and cannot interbreed.

The domestic goat has evolved several different styles of horn. Apart from the original scimitar horns of the wild ancestor, there are twisted straight horns, twisted "handle-bar" horns and no horns at all. Most of these are illustrated on artefacts of the region over the centuries. The scimitar shape seems to have been the inspiration for wild exaggeration at times and impossible goats with hugely curving spiralling horns adorn many a primitive plate or drinking vessel. The male goat, too, has something of a reputation for virility and promiscuity which seems to have followed him wherever goats are kept; the Greeks turned him into the God Pan, by no means a totally benign deity much given to orgies and seduction of maidens. Goats share with sheep some qualities of their milk; both are valued for the nutrition of invalids and children, made digestable because of the small size of the fat globules; and neither species is susceptible to tuberculosis which has caused much suffering in the past when bovine milk has been given to children.

The only commercial use for the hair of goats, apart from that of the specialist angora and mohair, seems to be the making of strong fabric and cord, and as such is commonly used for the black tents used by nomad peoples all over the Middle East.

WILD GOATS
(Capra aegrarus)

The PERSIAN IBEX *(Capra aegagrus)*, also known as the MOUNTAIN GOAT *(Boz e kouhi* or *Pazan* to the Persians), is an animal whose home is in the high rocks and mountains. Wherever such conditions can be found in Iran, there you can expect to see the Pazan. It is a distant ancestor of the domestic goat with a compact strong body, rather short legs and a black tail. A mature animal stands about 90 centimetres and may weigh 90 kilogrammes. The mature males grow a black beard and have a black shoulder stripe. They also possess a very distinguished pair of horns. The females have shorter horns and are often mistaken for the female Urial sheep.

Ibex, Central Elborz Protected area.　　　　　　　Photo: F. Shokraie

52

If threatened, ibex immediately take refuge among the rocks and climb to the highest points of vantage. A survey of Iranian mountain skylines will often reveal the majestic horns of a Pazan, standing balanced on a peak. Its strength, agility and beauty and its association with the highest crags gained it a special place among animals in ancient Persian art, even a pair of wings! Among the Luristan bronzes (1st to 2nd Century B.C.) were winged Mountain Goats, and this motif appears again in Achaeminid art. Objects made from bronze, or more rarely gold, appeared in the form of Luristan bits and horse harnesses or more sophisticated Achaeminid objects such as rhytons or handles of precious pots and jars. Even the head of a Griffin found on some Achaeminid rhytons was decorated with the segmented horns of an ibex. In even earlier times the animal appears on pottery from the neighbourhood of Susa (4th Century B.C.), some with remarkable detail such as exaggerated horns and beard.

Wild Goat   Illustration: E. Kahrom

The Pazan possesses all the attributes which are attractive to peoples who use animals as symbols. The Marlik civilisation (2nd Century B.C.) exploited this perhaps better than any other. The wild goat appears in many shapes and forms in the archeological discoveries of this era. The most remarkable and finest object known of them is a gold rhyton called *Afsaneh-e-zendezi* (The Story of Life). The stages of life are depicted in three rows around the rhyton. The bottom row shows the mother ibex suckling its kid. This scene is repeated many times round the rhyton. Above this the young ibex is browsing from a tree. It has short horns and is obviously immature. This too is repeated round the rhyton. The final stage of the animal's life is depicted in the top row, where the adult ibex is being hunted by a wild boar and vultures are flying in the sky.

Respect for this animal still exists among the Persians and there are many sayings and proverbs related to its agility and strength.

DEER

(Family: *Cervidae*)

Four species of deer have traditionally occupied differing habitats in Iran, from the lush green forests of the south Caspian coastal region to much drier areas in Khusistan province in the south-east.

In the dry areas of the Zagros foothills lived one of the rarest deer in the world. In the past, the natural vegetation consisted of forests of Tamarisk (manna), which has now disappeared and only survives along the banks of two rivers: the Dez and the Karke. These two narrow strips of vegetation are of paramount importance for the conservation of local communities of plants and animals.

The P E R S I A N   F A L L O W   D E E R   (*Dama mesopotamica*) was unknown to the west until recently. In former times it was quite common in Iran and countries south-east of the Mediterranean, and was a favourite subject for artists and craftsmen of the past.

The Y E L L O W   D E E R (Persian: *Gavazne zard*) found its way into Luristan bronzes, pottery and carpets. In particular, the well-known carvings and inscriptions of Taque-Bostan in Kermanshah are rich with hunting scenes involving this species, which is similar to the European Fallow Deer, apart from a larger body size and smaller antlers, and is easily identified.

The first western reports of this deer were received about 110 years ago (Harrington and Dareshoori, 1975), when the animal was present over a much wider range. At this time there were also some records of "a kind of deer with broad antlers" in the valleys of the Zagros mountains, and it is thought that these denoted the Persian Fallow Deer.

Unfortunately, loss of habitat and uncontrolled hunting led to a dramatic reduction in the population, to the extent that it was thought to be extinct. No record of its presence was made until about 40 years ago when a small group was found in the Tamarisk forests along the Karke River (now a Protected Area). It was immediately decided to try to save the species. A few animals were captured and sent to the Dasht-e-Naz Wildlife Refuge, an enclosed and fenced area in the Caspian forest; another small group was sent to Germany for propagation. Both groups are said to be doing well and the danger of extinction of this beautiful deer seems to be over.

The MARAAL, or PERSIAN RED DEER *(Cervus elaphos)* occupies habitats in the Caspian area. These areas are characterised by high mountains (the Elborz), and dense jungles of oaks, maples, Azedarach, etc., the autumn colour of which is a major attraction. Large mammals of the area include the Brown Bear *(Ursus arctos)*, wild boar *(Sus scrofa)*, leopards *(Panthera pardus)* and Red Deer (Persian *maraal*).

The wildlife habitats in the Caspian area are varied and can support a rich fauna. The southern coastal areas of the Caspian Sea once supported large populations of the Caspian Tiger *(Panthera tigris)* which is now believed to be extinct.

Red Deer devouring snake.   Photo: E. Kahrom

Most of the land between the Elborz Mountains and the sea is now cultivated, and this destruction of habitat together with uncontrolled hunting has led to the disappearance of the species. On the southern face of the Elborz, however, the natural habitats have not been affected as much as the northern ones. A large proportion of the original forests still exist and the important grasslands adjacent to the forests have not been much altered. These areas play a major role in the conservation of indigenous mammals who, though they also use the forest for shelter, generally feed on the out-lying grasslands.

Red Deer, in velvet.   Photo: E. Kahrom

The Red Deer is a good example of an animal associated with this sort of country. It is bigger than the European Red Deer, the males weighing up to 250 kilogrammes. The antlers are shed each spring and are commonly collected by trophy hunters; since ancient times they have been much in demand for the creation of artefacts such as knife and dagger handles. Some of the finest rugs, kelims and tapestry are produced in the areas around Gorgan, Gonbade-Quabous and Minoo-dasht. In particular, Turcomen *(Ghalicheh Torkaman)* rugs are much sought after. The Red Deer designs, and especially different interpretations of antlers, are used extensively, and are found in pottery excavated from ruins in the locality.

The Red Deer is greatly valued for its venison and the methods of hunting it have been well documented in early literature. At times, the hunters would imitate the roaring of the stags in rut, a hazardous procedure because it could also have the effect of attracting tigers, the other major predators of the Maraal.

In the well established thick forests of the Caspian region lives another species, the R O E D E E R *(Capreolus capreolus)* which has not attracted as much attention as the first two. It is extremely shy and rarely leaves the forest, consequently its numbers have been usually underestimated. The Persian name for the Roe is *Shouka* and limited numbers have been reported from the forests of Azerbaijan and Kurdistan in western Iran.

About thirty years ago an attempt was made to introduce the A X I S D E E R *(Axis axis)* into the forests of the southern Caspian region. The deer were obtained from India, but none have been seen since about ten years after the original introduction. No study was made of the effects of this on the other native species and it is possible that mortality of the new animals prevented a major ecological complication in the area.

GAZELLES

(Gazella)

The central area of Iran, between the mountains and the arid desert, consists of vast stretches of rolling hills and plains, reaching almost to the edge of the great central desert (Dasht-e-Kavir). The climate is favourable throughout the year, being less hot than the desert in summer and with a regular, if scanty, rainfall in the winter. The flora of this region is rich; the water supply is from rivers or quanats, and most of the great cities of Iran are located here.

Goitered Gazelle, Golestan National Park.　　　　Photo: F. Shokraie

This is the most favoured habitat of the GOITERED GAZELLE *(Gazella subgutturosa)*, Persian *Ahoo*. It is found in the plains of Khuzistan in the south-west, the plains of Zanjan in the north-west and Khorasan in the north-east and the Sistan plains in the south-east.

In the drier parts of the central desert is found the J E B E E R *(Gazella dorcas fuscifrons)* and very occasionally the two species can be seen together. A small population of the Goitered Gazelle is found on Kharg Island in the Persian Gulf.

The ahoo is an extremely elegant and beautiful animal, being about 75 centimetres high and weighing up to 50 kilogrammes. The males have a pair of slender pointed horns, bending slightly outwards at the tips. The females are usually hornless, but there is a small population of horned females in the west of Iran.

As mentioned previously, the Jebeer Gazelle lives in the arid region of the central Khavir. Smaller than the ahoo, it weighs up to 25 kilogrammes. Both sexes have horns and the species is only ever found in small groups of 20-30, unlike the ahoo which may run in herds of hundreds.

In the south-eastern plains another gazelle is prevalent. This is the C H I N K A R A   G A Z E L L E   *(Gazella dorcas bennetti)*, a very small animal, originating in India, and very handsome, with a reddish-brown coat. Although the horns are about the same size as those of the Jebeer, owing to the smaller body size they look bigger. The different sub-species of *dorcas* in the south-west of Iran are varied, and all interbreed; at least five different sub-species have been identified. In Iran the Goitered Gazelle is by far the most common; perhaps because of this, all gazelles usually go by the name of ahoo.

Chinkara Gazelle   Photo: Planet Earth / Anup Shah

For centuries Persians have been fascinated by this animal: artists, painters and poets have found inspiration in its beauty, and of course it has also been a favourite game species. Persian miniature paintings often depict riders in pursuit of gazelle, and even today the traditional methods are employed to hunt it. The ahoo, when chased, chooses an escape route but when in danger of being outrun, suddenly changes direction, usually across the line of the horsemen. The new direction can usually be predicted by a skilled huntsman, and the gazelle is more easily shot.

The poets and writers of Iran have used this behaviour as a metaphor for the sometimes irrational behaviour of their lovers. The saying "escaping like an ahoo" denotes that while someone may seem to be distancing themselves, he/she will eventually come back again. In other words, this is perhaps only a feigned escape! "What good news for the lonely, whose 'ahoo' is expected from far away" (Hafiz; trs. Kahrom).

There is story that a gazelle doe and her fawn were being chased by a horseman in Khorasan and took refuge in the house of the Imam Reza (the 8th Imam, who is buried in Mashad). He saved the animals and ever since then no right-thinking hunter will pursue a doe gazelle with her fawn.

The Pahlavans in Firdawsi's *Shahnama* enjoyed hunting the gazelle, and chasing it in its vast and beautiful habitat was a favourite pastime. Bows and arrows or the lassoo were the principal methods, and lassooing gazelle was taught to nobles' children as part of their education. The hero Rustam had a unique method of gazelle-hunting peculiar to himself, or rather his horse, Raksh, who could outrun them. On one occasion Raksh pointed to a gazelle and promised it to Rustam who gave him the following advice: "Do not give away a free ahoo until you have caught him." This popular proverb is still quoted today. Cheetahs were also used for gazelle hunting.[5]

The beauty and elegance of the gazelle in its habitat, the harmony with which it blends into its surroundings and the sheer magic of seeing a herd in such surroundings has inspired poets through the ages. One poem by Rumi tells the story of a captured gazelle being taken and stabled with a herd of donkeys. The gazelle refuses all food offered to him and the donkeys think he is being snobbish. The gazelle protests that he is indeed different from them; he has grazed lush and wonderful pastures and has eaten herbs no donkey ever knew. Rumi concludes that the gazelle suffers among lesser animals, as a man of refinement suffers among those of coarser upbringing.

---

[5] Unfortunately these methods of hunting have been supplanted in modern times by chases to exhaustion by motor vehicles and guns, even machine guns. Artificial wells are dug to attract the animals in numbers so that the slaughter can be greater. These methods are cruel and should be banned. Owing to conservation measures the total population numbers are in no danger at the present time.

The modern poet Mordab ("Marsh") F. Farokhzad compares the freedom of movement and gallantry of the life of the gazelle with the stressed and sordid life of modern man:

Oh you gazelles of the plains
Who roam the wilderness as you wish,
If on your way you find a river
In which the flow of water is whispering a melody
In which the silk of water is flowing to the richness of the seas,
If on your plain you see the breezes and the beautiful face of the
     moon,
If you see the grass blown by the wind and the scattered perfume
     of the bushes and flowers,
And if you see the generous reflection of the sun in your
     homeland;
Remember the sleeplessness of those under duress
Remember Death in the marshes.

(trs. Kahrom)

CATTLE AND BUFFALOS

(Family: *Bovidae*)

Iran today is not prime cattle country; it is largely too dry and too hot for cattle to thrive, but nevertheless cattle have been used by Man in the regions historically connected with the Persian empires. The ancestral wild form of cattle, *Bos primigenius* or "Auroch", was hunted by early man; it was a very large animal with immense horns, and

63

almost certainly was hunted to extinction by the Assyrians in the heyday of their power. The last reported wild bull hunt was one by Ashurnasipal, 884-860 B.C. (Epstein and Mason, 1984).

Long before this though, domesticated cattle were being used for the purposes for which we use them today. The early Sumerians had milking parlours and depicted their cattle being milked from behind as is the practice with sheep; this may have been because they seem to have had a very small breed of cow, which would have been difficult to milk from the side. Apart from these homely scenes however, the main interest seems to have been the bulls, which were adopted very early as symbols of power. Ever since those times, bulls have appeared on every sort of artefact, sometimes as themselves, as for instance the bull's head decoration on the inlaid harp found in the Royal tombs at Ur, or else in conflict with another fierce beast, usually a lion. The combined symbol of a bull being attacked by a lion which is leaping on its hindquarters, recurs throughout ancient history, with some fine examples to be seen in the reliefs on the processional way at Persepolis. It is unclear quite what this symbol means, possibly good triumphing over evil, or day over night, or maybe there was a more political significance.

Much of the importance of cattle in early times lay in their use as draught animals, and they were the principal motive power for the agriculture of the area. Hammurabi (c. 950 B.C.) laid down sets of rules about the uses of oxen; for instance, hired oxen had to be returned in the condition in which the hirer found them. If they were damaged in any way, the hirer had to make good that damage. He was not to be blamed for accidents however, such as an ox dropping dead or being killed by a lion (obviously divine intervention). Owners of oxen had to restrain dangerous animals, with the proviso that the owner was not at fault if the animal had shown no previous aggressive tendency. This legal principle is enshrined in British law to this day, in the case of dogs, which with the exception of certain known dangerous breeds, are allowed "the first bite".

Threshing grain was a common task performed by oxen in the ancient world; the principle of fairness to the workers was enshrined in the Biblical injunction "thou shalt not muzzle the ox that treads the corn". A rather similar Persian proverb has it that "threshing is no job for a goat; it requires a strong ox and an experienced man". It is often used when an amateur attempts a task that is obviously too much for him.

As well as being draught animals, oxen were used in ancient times for riding; a painted pot from the Sava area of c. 13th Century A.D. shows a decorated animal with a female rider attended by a groom.

The status of cattle seems to have fluctuated a good deal over the historical timespan. At the time of the Arab invasion there was a common belief that the heavens were supported by a cow, and that the earth itself was balanced on the tip of the cow's horn; every so often the cow shifted the burden onto the other horn, which gave rise to earthquakes. This idea is reflected in some of the poetry of Omar Khayam. The generally reverent attitude to cattle was shared by some of the early Islamic preachers; the Imam Ali in a well-known saying ("hadith") suggests that there were no prouder race of animals than cattle until the Children of Israel started to worship them, whereupon they became so ashamed that they bowed their heads to the ground and have done so ever since.[6]

Later, the heavenly image of the cow deteriorated, and it became notorious for its appetite and sloth. The poet Rumi has a story about a

---

[6] This is possibly a reference to Aaron's Golden Calf.

cow living on a very lush island, who dreamed every night that she had eaten the island bare and was likely to starve. However, the next morning the vegetation was as luxuriant as ever; the moral being that even though human beings have always been provided for in the past, they still worry about the future.

The cow (Persian: *gaav*) has a secure place in Persian folk-lore. In one of the tales of the Mullah Nasreldin, the Mullah surpasses the cow's stupidity by his own. A cow trying to extract a morsel from a large earthenware pot, gets her head stuck inside it. To save the jar, the Mullah cuts off the cow's head, and finds he still has to smash the pot to get the head out.

Lastly, there is a somewhat improbable injunction that one should try to imitate the cow's graceful gait, as it is one of the finest animals in this matter of locomotion, a distinction it apparently shares with the partridge!

WATER BUFFALO
(Family: *Bovidae; Bubalus bubalus*)

The Asian Water Buffalo is a common domestic animal in all parts of the continent which have plentiful supplies of water and a warm or hot climate, although they can survive cold winters by growing a hairy coat, as happens in some parts of Turkey. Normally they have very little body hair, but are usually large, fat, rather sluggish animals, with large flattened horns which grow out nearly horizontally, turning upwards near the tips.

In spite of living in hot countries they cannot stand much direct sun, but take refuge from it by wallowing in mud or submerging themselves entirely in water. They graze water vegetation and other poor quality fodder, and are thus much less demanding to look after than dairy cows. In spite of this, they are good milkers, and are kept for this purpose along with draught animals in paddy fields and coconut plantations, etc.

Generally, they have gentle, quiet temperaments and are easy to train, often carrying the children of their owners on their heads or backs. They are usually considered too valuable to be used for meat in the usual way, but nevertheless have a good growth rate and could be profitably raised for that purpose.

According to Ross Cockrill (1984) the F.A.O. estimate of the Iranian population of water buffalos in 1982 was 228,000, only slightly less than that of Iraq, where the main concentration was in the marshes of the Euphrates/Tigris Delta.

Water Buffalo in Hooralazim marshes.   Photo: E. Kahrom

It is probable that the animal was first domesticated from the wild, either there or in the Indus valley sometime prior to 2500 B.C. There is not a great deal of archaeological evidence of the early domestication of this impressive animal apart from a few seals and bone fragments. The great Sumerian king Gilgamesh is credited with having subjugated wild buffalo, and the Assyrians also slaughtered many in their usual way. The Persian King, Khosraw II, is depicted hunting buffalo on a silver chased plate (now in the Bibliotheque Nationale, Paris) which dates from the 7th Century A.D.

Nowadays buffalo are kept on a ranching system in the few areas of Iran which are suitable for them, i.e. in the marshlands of Baluchistan and Abadan and in some of the lower-lying Caspian districts. Here, contrary to the tradition of surrounding countries, they are used for their meat. They can be quite a spectacular sight in large herds, and are often attended by flocks of egrets, attracted by the ticks and insects which parasitise them.

ELEPHANT

(Family: *Proboscidae*)

INDIAN ELEPHANT *(Elephas maximus)* and AFRICAN ELEPHANT *(Loxodonta africana)*

The historical aspects of the use of elephants in the Near and Middle East have been admirably chronicled by Scullard (1974), and it is to this work that the reader who wishes to gain more detailed information should refer.

Elephants were hunted by the Egyptian Pharaohs Thutmose I and his grandson Thutmose II c. 1550 B.C. through Syria to the Euphrates, and some at least were captured. A painting in the tomb of the vizier Rekhmire of that time shows what is very clearly an Asian elephant. The Assyrian king Tiglath-pileser I recorded that he had slaughtered ten mighty male elephants and taken four alive, and brought the hides, tusks and live animals to Assur. Assurnasirpal II seems not only to have hunted elephants but established a sort of elephantine safari-park. Part of the tribute that the Israelite king Jehu paid to Shalmaneser III included an elephant "from the land of Musri", which is thought to have been in the Persian Gulf area, and thus of Asian origin.

The fact that there were enough elephants in the region to hunt tells us something about the climate and ecology of the time. Elephants consume large amounts of vegetation daily in order to live; this means that there must have been a great deal of semi-tropical, or at least temperate forest for them to live in. According to Smidt (1986), a mature elephant spends about 18 hours a day feeding, and consumes some 280 kilogrammes of vegetation in that time. It also needs 140-200 litres of water. The Asian elephant is also known to be susceptible to heat stroke. Syria was always a great exporter of timber, but its forests and elephants were ruthlessly exploited by Man, and wild elephants seem to have become extinct there by about 500 A.D.

Craftsmen from Phoenicia and Syria were skilled in carving ivory, and some fine examples of their work have been found in the Assyrian palaces at Nimrud and elsewhere. The Mediterranean civilisations of the period were also very partial to ivory carvings and the north African elephant population, which was once very high, also seems to have been wiped out by the end of the 4th Century A.D.

Elephants were used in warfare during much of the early history of the Middle East. They had the advantage of being terrifying to the opposition and, rather like camels, apt to panic the enemy's cavalry, but they had the great disadvantage of being somewhat given to panic themselves, so that if one or two were wounded in the first attack they were liable to retreat precipitately through their own ranks, causing chaos as they went. It was eventually realised that one way to defeat elephants was to blind them; a courageous soldier armed with a long spear could achieve this very well. After this became generally known, elephants were used much less for the actual fighting and more as baggage animals and transporters of heavy equipment. In his battle against Alexander the Persian king Darius had 15 elephants stationed on the front line. However, they seem to have taken no part in the battle and are not mentioned again in Alexander's account of it. They may have been merely intended to frighten Alexander's horses. Later, presents of elephants were sent to Alexander in the hope of appeasing him, and during his expeditions into India and Afghanistan he became very familiar with their use. His greatest battle was against Porus at Hydaspes (326 B.C.). Porus was said to have had a huge army including 200 elephants but was defeated by Alexander by superior generalship when he sent his men to encircle individual beasts and engage them. The elephants only retreated slowly, but then began to cause damage to their own side. Porus fled wounded on his elephant, and eventually slid off to the ground. Later, Alexander treated him as a hero, and restored him to his kingdom.

The Persians continued to use elephants when engaged with wars against the Romans. The Sassanian king Ardeshir seems to have revived the idea of having an elephant corps. In 230 A.D. he started besieging Nisibis. The Romans sent a large force commanded by Severus

Alexander, but the engagement seems to have been indecisive or even a Roman defeat. At any rate, Severus left the east and is said to have had a chariot pulled by four elephants for his "triumph" in Rome. Ardeshir's son, Shapur, also fought against the Romans but was defeated by Gordian III at Rasaina. Gordian is said to have sent a number of elephants to Rome, but was murdered before he could return himself. The Emperor Philip held Games in 248 A.D. to celebrate the Roman millennium at which most of Gordian's collection of wild animals, including 32 elephants, was killed.

Shapur II used elephants very effectively against Julian in the war of 363 A.D., and later used them against the Armenians. In 502 A.D. the Persian king Kawad (Cobades) invaded Roman Armenia and entered the captured city of Amida riding an elephant. His successor, Kosraw, was at war with the Empire during most of Justinian's reign, and in 544 A.D. laid siege to Edessa, where the inhabitants held a squealing pig over the wall, which so upset the war elephant taking part that it retreated out of control. Kosraw, even when over eighty years of age, was still fighting the Romans, but was defeated at Melitene (573. A.D.). He escaped by crossing the Euphrates on the back of his elephant, and 24 captured elephants were sent to Constantinople. The Emperor Heraclius finally forced the Persians back and captured the great park at Dastigerd, where the Persians kept many animals, including, it was said, 900 elephants. This, though, was at the end of the period of power for both Persians and Romans; afterwards the Barbarians and Arabs took over the Roman and Persian Empires.

Elephants were well known to the people of Persia through legend and reputation, though probably very few of them had ever actually seen one. The stories concerning them are as wonderful and improbable as the animals themselves.

Elephantine transport   Photo: E. Kahrom

A story about Rustam, in Firdawsi's *Shahnama*, relates that his father's great white elephant, on which he had gone in to battle, went mad (probably the condition known as *Musht* in male elephants) and had broken loose and was causing havoc in the district. Against all advice Rustam sought out the dangerous beast and slew it with one blow of his mace, thereby gaining a reputation for himself as "a mighty man of valour". In a later episode Rustam lassooed the Emperor of China during a battle, and dragged him down from his elephant, leading Firdawsi to philosophise about being one moment on the top of world and the next utterly cast down.

The general extraordinariness of the elephant was expressed well in an account by Rumi of a group of people who touched an elephant in total darkness and were then entirely unable to agree what sort of animal it was that they had been handling. Saadi's advice on friendship is pertinent: "If you befriend an elephant-driver you must be sure your home is big enough to accept the elephant as well". A homesick Persian will say "the elephant misses India"

There are a number of illustrations of richly decorated elephants with riders among the pottery excavated from Rayy and Sava (13th Century A.D.). On one of them the richness of the trappings possibly denotes a wedding procession.

WILD BOAR

(Sus scrofa; Family: *Suidae)*

The ancestor of the domestic pig is a resilient species which can adapt to several types of habitat, from sparse forest to jungle and swamp. It breeds very rapidly, having large litters of striped piglets and has a diet of fruits, acorns, fungi, etc.; otherwise unexploited by other woodland animals. In many parts of the world it is considered a major pest for its forays on cornfields and gardens, which a small herd of wild swine can devastate in a night. If surprised or cornered it is a dangerous oponent and has never been high on the list of Man's favourite animals. It is not adapted to a desert or nomadic existence and both the Judaic and Islamic traditions have prohibited its use as food. This apparently divine injunction is in fact a very worthwhile piece of early food hygiene, as swine commonly harbour a parasitic worm in their muscles *(Trichina spiralis)* which is pathogenic to Man and only destroyed by

73

thorough cooking, which is difficult in desert conditions. It seems to have lent itself to domestication fairly early on in terms of Middle Eastern history, some of the few remains of pigs found in the Sumerian archeological excavations being too small to be those of wild boar. (Epstein and Bichard, 1984). The wild boar hunt seems to have been an exciting business, necessitating numbers of men, horses and hounds. The well known rock relief at Taquue-e-Bustam shows such a hunt taking place in marshes, possibly those of the Tigris/Euphrates Delta, where a large population of wild boar have lived almost to this day (Maxwell, 1957; Thesiger, 1984).

Wild Boar.   Photo: Aquila Photographics / Reinhard Siegel

Interestingly, the hunters of the boar are shown mounted on elephants, which were possibly the only steeds capable of progress in the swamps. In Iran, the chief predator of these wild pigs was the lion, which inhabited roughly the same habitat. It is debatable as to whether it was the diminution of the wild boar populations or the destruction of habitat that was the ultimate cause of the extermination of the predator; nor in fact, does it matter, because the loss of habitat would have led to the same outcome in any case.

Swine have managed to adapt better to persecution and habitat change, and are still found in the scrubby forests of the mountain regions of Iran, where they remain a nuisance to the peasant farmers, in spite of the cold winters and lack of cover normally required by a forest animal. Within recent times a group of Christian Armenians exploited the meat obtained from wild boar and engaged in a lucrative trade in sausages, kebabs, etc.

CASPIAN TIGER

(*Panthera tigris*; Persian: *Babr*)

It is perhaps poignant that the section on Carnivores should begin with the two greatest and most beautiful of them, and that both the lion and the tiger are now extinct in Iran.

The tiger roamed the southern coastal areas of the Caspian Sea, parts of Afghanistan and southern districts of Russia until relatively recently. The last one was seen some forty years ago, having become extinct in Afghanistan well before that time. Conscious that no-one seemed to have encountered tigers for some time, an extensive search was mounted by biologists and Game Wardens, using baits and automatic cameras, etc; but no evidence of living animals was found.

Skins and photographs show the Caspian tiger to have been rather lighter in colour and generally larger than the Indian variety and more nearly like the Siberian one. The last sighting of the Caspian tiger was in about 1954 in what is now the Golestan National Park. Habitat destruction, over-hunting and deliberate poisoning by stock-keeping farmers are undoubtedly the reasons why it is no longer with us.

Knowledge of the tiger and its habits were quite localised in Iran. Its common title *Babre-Mazanderan* relates to one Province only, and elsewhere it was often confused with other species such as the leopard. The Iranian national sport of wrestling has been enriched by participants from Mazanderan, and a wrestler of international reputation may gain the honorific title of *Babre-Mazanderan.*

Tiger skins were much in demand in former times for armour; they were known as *Babre bayan* and are mentioned in the *Shahnama.* In modern Persian *Pooste Babr* (tiger skin) denotes authority and influence while conversely *Babre-kaghazi* (paper tiger) or *Babre-poushally* (straw tiger) implies the appearance of power only without the substance. Like the lion, the tiger has given its name to various people and places – Babran, Babroz, Babrak, etc. Tigers appear among other animals in some of the illustrated scenes from stories, and some of the various divs and demons who also figure in these works are suspiciously stripey and fanged. One may surmise that the aura of fierceness properly belonging to the tiger rubbed off into Iranian demonology of the time. A surprising place to see tigers is on the front of a mosque, but a mosque at Samarkand, formerly in the Persian domain, carries two very fine tigers above its portals. As Tamerlane is considered to have commissioned this mosque and many other works in Samarkand, perhaps it was as a ravening tiger that he wished to be remembered. Aganst this, it must be said that the tigers in question look very aimiable and jolly, perhaps only cubs. Each one is following what is probably a wild sheep.

LION

(Panthera leo Persica; Persian: *Shir)*

The Persian lion is the same species as the Asian lion of India. There are no remains, or even photographs of the Persian lion, but it seems to have been black-maned, and differing from the African species in that the mane of the male does not cover the forehead, and having thicker abdominal skin. Its principal habitat was the forested region of south-west Iran and the riverine forests of Khuzistan. The last lions were recorded in the early 1940s, single specimens being seen by Heaney (1943) and Champion-Jones (1945) who saw a lioness in the Karhk River Gorge in 1941; it is probable that a few survived later. The main prey was the wild boar, but other species such as deer, onager and gazelle were also taken. The reed-beds of the Arzan Plain to the south of Shiraz were also well known for their lion populations. This area is now a National Park and in 1977 a project was proposed to restock the area with lions, using animals obtained from the Gir Forest Park in India (Mountfort, pers comm). This proved to be extremely controversial, and its viability was questioned on both social and scientific grounds.

As the project involved buying land from local farmers and then resettling them elsewhere, much anger was aroused in the human population. The scientific justification was also queried because of the general problem of the introduction of an exotic species into an environment that might not be suitable for it. In fact, such an environment no longer exists in Iran, and without much work to provide a good habitat, any reintroduction attempt is bound to fail. In the event, Project Lion was never completed, and although the Arzan National Park continues to exist, it is without lions.

Although the lion is physically extinct, it still lives in the fertile imaginations of the Persians. Its name, *Shir*, has been incorporated into place-names, such as Shiraz, Shir-kuh (Lion Mountain), Shir-rud (Lion River), Tange-shir (Pass of the Lion), etc. Wherever the name occurs it denotes bravery and dignity.

Etymologically, there are known to be similarities between some Persian words and English ones, i.e. *mader* = mother, *dochter* = daughter. *Shir* may also be such a word = sir, sire, shire, etc.)

The lion as a symbolic national animal is also common to both Persian and English cultures, and until recently a lion bearing a sword was depicted on the Iranian national flag. However, lion imagery is very ancient. Early civilisations such as the Hittite and Assyrian were in the habit of placing immense stone lions to guard entrances to cities, processional ways, etc.; often they were supplied with a human head and a pair of wings. Such lions were the surrogates of powerful gods who it was intended should look after the city, and deter enemies.

The "Lion of Babylon", still situated among the ruins of that city, is a massive stone beast standing over a prostrate human form. The local archeological opinion is that it is not of local origin however, but may have been part of the war booty from some long forgotten campaign.

The Assyrians, whose kings seem to have combined savagery and cruelty with love of the Arts and Literature, have left us the most potent of lion images in their portrayals of lion hunting, so beautifully delineated in the carved reliefs now dispersed in museums of the

The Lion of Babylon.   Photo: P. N. Humphreys

world. The artists who executed these were in a class of their own. They captured not only the magnificent savagery of the animals as they leapt upon horses or men, but the beauty and pathos of the dying lionesses, stuck full of spears but still formidable as they struggled to inflict a last blow on their tormentors.

Lions were an important part of ancient establishment cultural activity. Kings maintained stocks of lions, partly for organised hunting excursions when a number of lions would be released on which the nobles and courtiers could demonstrate their manly prowess. The lions seem to have been fed on a mixed diet of animal carcases and unwanted people, such as criminals, political enemies and similar encumbrances. The prophet Daniel would have been one such intended victim, but in his case the lions lacked appetite and he emerged from the den uneaten. Indeed, there seems at times to have been almost an urban lion problem. "The slothful saith 'there is a lion in the streets'" (Proverbs 26:13). The hero Samson made his reputation by slaying a wandering lion with "the jaw-bone of an ass". It would have been a tactful move for a vassal king to present the Emperor with a lion cub or two for his collection, as well as implying the nobility and strength of the recipient through the nature of the gift.

The cult of the lion has, of course, not just been confined to Persia and her neighbours, but has been taken up with enthusiasm by European and Chinese cultures, to which it can hardly have been a very familiar animal in the flesh. Be that as it may, there is no more gratifying symbolic animal with which to be associated than the lion. Great strength combined with an impressive appearance and the reputation of being ferocious in defence make it the ideal animal to emulate in matters political and ceremonial. No wonder it has remained so popular.

Persian tradition held that the crown could only be obtained by a hero who could snatch it from a throne to which two lions were chained. Bahram-Gur became king by killing the lions and seizing the crown. Lions were highly regarded as guards not only of earthly palaces but as defences against the forces of darkness generally, and stone lions still guard cemetaries at Hamadan (Shir-e-Sangi) and Bushir.

There is a tale ascribed to the poet Rumi about a man who wished to have a lion tattooed between his shoulders but who shouted so much at every prick of the needle that the tattooist gave up, suggesting that anyone who wanted to pretend to be like a lion, should be able to put up with a few needles!

Ladies' Polo

Bearded tit   Photo: Aquila Photographics / K. Careson

Mountainous country, West Iran   Photo: E. Kahrom

Roller   Photo: Aquila Photographics

Hoopoe   Photo: Aquila Photographics

Bee-eater   Photo: E. Kahrom

Peacock carpet design

Photo: E. Kahrom

Wildlife habitat at sunset

Photo: E. Kahrom

Hunting scene from Persian Miniature 16th Century

Photo: E. Kahr

Common Jackal

Photo: Aquila Photographics / M. Lane

Brown Bears

Photo: Aquila Photographics / R. Maier

Mountainous country West Iran

Photo: Aquila Photographics / R. Siegel

shtar Gate from Babylon (now in Berlin)   Photo: P. N. Humphreys

Tigers pursuing wild sheep on mosque portal at Samarkand

Photo: P. N. Humphre

Contemporary lion carpet

Photo: E. Kahr

Lion-headed Rhyton.   Photo: E. Kahrom

Roman Emperor Valerian pays homage to the Emperor Shapur

(see page 23)   *Photo: P. N. Humphreys*

Early donkey transport *(see page 34)*

Photo: E. Kahrom

The Persian proverb-makers made good use of lions: "The prince of animals is the lion, the meanest the ass; nevertheless, an ass who carries loads is better than a lion who kills men"; "It is not wise to declare war on a lion alone, but united even ants can skin a lion"; and "Need transforms formidable lions into mean and cunning foxes." One could add the Biblical one "A living dog is better than a dead lion."

The favourite romantic tale of Majnoon and Leila has been illustrated in countless miniatures and carpets, especially the episode where Majnoon resorts to the wilderness and recounts the story of his love for Leila to the wild animals who are so charmed by the tale that they cease from strife among themselves and gather round the desperate youth in perfect harmony. Illustrations of this type form a valuable record of the species that were familiar to Persians in the past.

Another type of record is that provided by explorers and travellers to the country, especially in the 19th Century. Arnold (1877) tells of an attack on another explorer, the scientist W. T. Blandford, in 1867 in Arzan. Although Blandford escaped up a tree, his horse, which was probably the main target, was wounded. By the time Crawshay-Williams visited Iran (which he referred to as the land of the lion and the sun) in 1903, lions were thought to be extinct even in the Arzan region (Crawshay-Williams, 1907). Attacks on people or domestic animals may have been partially triggered by shortage of wild game

The famous lion carpets of Iran (Bagh-e-vahsh = zoo or garden carpets) often contain other carnivores such as leopards, together with numerous gazelle and deer. They are still being made, with modern styles coming into use as well as the more traditional designs.

A traditional story tells of a leopard who reached the highest peak of the mountain and was then annoyed to find something else above himself, namely, the full moon. Flushed with anger, he leaped at it with the intention of bringing it down, and thus ensured his own demise through arrogance.

The widespread distribution of the leopard is reflected in the numbers of "leopard hills" *(palang-kuh)* to be found throughout Persia, and Firdawsi recounts that leopard-skin tunics and drum-covers were customary in military ceremonial parades. The skin patterns of the leopard have been used by Persian artists as much as those of other cultures. A curious expression of this was found in pottery at Rayy (12th Century) where the spots have the form of roses and the claws as the thorns of the rose.

Onager – common prey of the leopard   Illustration: E. Kahrom

WOLF

(Canis lupus; Persian: Gorg)

The wolf does not enjoy a very enviable reputation, and wolves in Persia are no exception. Although the ecological importance of this animal is recognised by zoologists, it still inspires fear and even hatred in the ordinary person. Although most people in Iran have never encountered a wolf, still less listened to a pack of wolves howling (the true sound of "the wilderness"), Persian children learn to dread the wolf almost as soon as they can talk. Persian nursery tales are awash with accounts of delightful cuddly lambs being devoured by the aggressive and deceitful wolf; often this is said to be because the lamb had committed some wicked crime, like not listening to his parents. The wolf is another archetypal model for demons or even the Angel of Death. "The Assyrians came down like the Wolf on the fold" from *The Destruction of Sennacherib* by Lord Byron, is a favourite poem among most English children: they can feel the ruthlessness in that first line, although they are even less likely to have seen a wolf than Persian children. Be that as it may, shepherds have dreaded the approach of winter in most regions of the Middle East when hunger may drive the wolves from the hills to seek easier meat. The great mastiff-like dogs which guard the nomads' camps are there to repel wolves as well as human strangers, and many a tale of their gallantry and self-sacrifice has been told round the camp-fires at night.

Packs of wolves are said to cooperate among themselves, leaving some of their members to attack and divert the dogs while another sneaks in and makes off with a juicy kid. Some villagers construct great thorny fences to enclose their flocks at night; these sheep-folds can be seen in many upland parts of the region. This practice has led to speculation that the Birth of Christ, with its attendant "shepherds in the fields with their flocks by night" must have been at some other season than winter, when no sensible shepherds would have been abroad with sheep running the risk of wolf attack.

Wolves are very versatile and adaptable animals and occupy a wide range of habitats in all the provinces of Iran. They are also variable in size and colour, the largest being found in the north. Adult males may reach 75 kilogrammes and may be as much as 180 centimetres long from nose to tail-tip.

Wolves are gregarious and intelligent animals, living in small or large packs. It is thought that the food supply largely regulates the size of the packs; thus, in a desert area where food is scarce there may be no more than two in a pack, whereas in more favourable places there may be as many as nine. In the northern mountainous districts wild sheep are a common prey, but deer and wild boar are also taken. If this type of prey becomes scarce the wolves easily take to smaller mammals and rodents, as they do elsewhere in the world.

Attacks by wolves on man and his domestic animals are in fact extremely rare, and are believed to be nearly always brought about by pressure of hunger due to deep snow cover, the older animals succumbing to the need to eat first. Ecologically, wolves act as regulators of herbivore populations and weed out the unfit.

This side of the wolves' role in the natural scene is not yet apparent to many people, who possibly prefer the more sinister and exciting image and have a number of sayings to back them up: "Teach the wolf to sew; he already knows how to tear"; and according to Saadi, "Even if a wolf-cub is reared by a man, it will eventually become a wolf and will not heed him".

A piece of advice for a ruler suggests, "Do not be too soft or show too much mercy: because then the sharp-toothed wolf becomes impudent."

CHEETAH

(*Acinonyx jubatus*; Persian: *Youz palang*)

The Persian name translates appropriately as the Greyhound-Leopard or Hunting-Leopard. Cheetahs hunt by running down their prey at high speed. They are not nearly as powerful as the leopard and have shorter, non-retractable claws, which means that they cannot climb and have to eat as much as possible of their prey at once, as they cannot store it in a tree like leopards can. Cheetahs are found in Asia and Africa and were thought to be all genetically the same, in other words, a clone. However, this may not be strictly true. Instead of rosettes like those of the leopard, the spots of the cheetah are solid. Another peculiarity lies in their memories. They are difficult to breed in captivity, a settled pair spending years together without producing young. Research by the Zoological Society of London found it was necessary to split up a pair at intervals and then re-introduce them to each other months later when the novelty of the "new" mate would immediately initiate breeding activity. And whereas a tame tiger would remember a familiar person for years, cheetahs seem to forget their handlers and rearers in a very short space of time (D. M. Jones pers. comm).

Cheetah.   Photo: Aquila Photographics / Hanne & Jens Eriksen

In former times cheetahs were trained for hunting gazelle; training methods seem to have been of dubious humanity, on the lines of falconry, by a mixture of confinement, starvation and familiarity with man: often a combination of cheetahs and falcons would be used in a hunt. (Cornish, 1902). Cheetahs are no longer used in this way, but on the other hand, Iran may be the only Asian country to support a breeding population. It is fortunate in still having some large areas of dry land available for conservation of the typical open plain species. The Khoush Yeilagh Wildlife Refuge is at the northern end of the Touran Protected Area (c. 2 million hectares). Both prey and predator species have increased in numbers since this great area was designated, and the present population of cheetah is at a satisfactory level and is not thought to be in any danger. If, however, tourism should become an industry in Iran as it has in Africa, care will have to be taken to avoid disturbance, as the cheetah is a very shy and sensitive animal and is known to desert its cubs when upset by intrusion of tourist vehicles (Edington and Edington, 1986).

The 11th Century poet, F. Gogani, compares the cheetah's pursuit of game with the inevitability of Death pursuing Life:

The world is awaiting our death day and night,
Like the Cheetah in pursuit of the Gazelle.

FOXES

(Vulpes vulpes; Persian: *Rubah)*

Although there are four different species of fox in Iran the C O M M O N F O X *(Vulpes Vulpes)* is the most widespread and is the species most usually meant when foxes are referred to. It inhabits most parts of the country except very dense forest and the dry parts of the Central Desert and the Kavir in the south. In these dry areas its place is taken by *Ruppell's Fox.*

The Common Fox varies considerably in coat colour and may range from dark brown to almost white. It is an omnivorous animal and will eat almost anything from beetles, rodents, birds and vegetable matter including fruit. Its fondness for poultry and the sometimes ingenious manner in which it obtains them has given it the reputation for craftiness. In Persian, the adjective *makkar,* meaning deceitful, calculating and cunning, almost always accompanies a discussion concerning foxes, in that way not differing from the English use of foxy and foxiness.

Common Fox   Photo: R. Ghaemi

In the south-eastern parts of the Caspian area, the vast Gorgan Plains, spread towards the north and the Turkmen Plains of Russia. These are fertile agricultural areas with an alkaline soil, and are ecologically very similar. A fascinating animal of this region is the C O R S A C F O X *(Vulpes corsac)*, also to be found in eastern Iran. It is a small fox, which hunts small mammals and rodents. Being shy and nocturnal, its numbers are often underestimated and it is usually outnumbered by the Common Fox. It is known to the local people as *rubah-e-sardom siah* or "the fox with the black tip to its tail". The coat colour is a silvery grey which matches the soil colour of the region.

The DESERT or RUPPELL'S FOX *(Vulpes Ruppelli)* is a creature of the dryest and hottest parts of Iran, and one could be forgiven for imagining that no animals could exist in these hostile, dry environments; however, there are some animals which have evolved strategies to conserve water; for example, becoming entirely nocturnal and living by day in a subterraneon burrow, as well as certain other physiological adaptions. Ruppell's Fox is thus a typical desert animal. Small (up to 3 kilogrammes), sandy in colour, it has large ears for the detection of its prey at night. It lives on small desert rodents such as jerboas and jirds as well as ground-nesting birds, reptiles, insects and plants. Water is provided entirely in the food taken.

One of the rarest foxes in the world inhabits the mountainous areas of Kerman and Fars. This is BLANDFORD'S FOX *(Vulpes cana)* known in Persian as the *Shah Rubah* or King Fox from its distinguished appearance, bearing as it does a reddish body with a black mane and thick and bushy tail.

As in other cultures the fox seems to have assumed the position of Court Jester: puny, but wise, cunning and occasionally comic. Its Persian nick-name *Agha Rubah* (Mr. Fox) says it all.

Saadi has a tale about a man who saw a fox running to hide itself. "Why are you running off?" said the man. "Because," replied the fox, "I have heard they are forcing the camels to work". "But you are not a camel." "Be quiet!" the fox said. "If the envious and jealous say I am a camel and I am caught, who is going to believe me and enquire into my real nature?"

Another story by Rumi has it that the kingly lion went hunting with his two viziers, the wolf and the fox. They killed a buffalo, a goat and a rabbit. The lion told the wolf to share out the kill between them.

The wolf allocated the buffalo to the lion, the tasty goat to himself and the rabbit to the fox. The lion was extremely angry at this result and felled the wolf with a blow of his paw, complaining that even in his royal presence the wolf could only think of his own benefit. "Now you do it," he told the fox. The fox bowed and replied, "The buffalo is for your breakfast, you could have the goat for lunch and, if you wish, you could have rabbit for supper." This pleased the lion exceedingly and he said, "You have indeed done justice, I am impressed with your excellent judgement. Tell me from whom did you get this knowledge?" The fox replied, "Your majesty, I learned it from the fate of the wolf."

JACKALS AND HYAENAS

THE GOLDEN JACKAL
(Canis aureus; Persian: *Shoghal)*

The howling of jackals is one of the most remarkable wildlife sounds in the Iranian countryside. Many of the early European travellers complained bitterly about the noise jackals made, which kept them awake (Ousely, 1823). According to Persian tradition, jackals once lived in the towns and dogs in the wilderness. Finally the dogs persuaded the jackals that they should take a holiday in the country. Having once got the jackals out in the open air, the dogs took up their easy billets in the towns and have remained there ever since. Every evening the jackals howl to be let back in, and the dogs reply denying them. The close relationship between dogs and jackals is recognised in the proverbial saying "Yellow dog is the jackal's brother", which is used when two dissimilar people or phenomena share the same bad quality.

Jackals do not enjoy a very savoury reputation, especially among the farmers and peasants, being accused of killing poultry and even lambs. Although found in every province they are perhaps most numerous in the Caspian region, where they can be found on rubbish tips and around carcasses of animals thrown up on the beach. Where plentiful, they frequently become road traffic casualties. Closely associated with Man, they haunt villages and do some damage to the vine and melon crops in nearby fields, so that baiting and trapping become necessary to keep numbers in check.

The Mazanderan Plains have always been a favourite habitat for the jackal and there is a piece of folk-wisdom which says that "Mazanderan jackals can only be caught by Mazanderan dogs", implying the great value of local knowledge. The jackal in appearance looks much like a small wolf, but with a redder coat.

Rumi has a jackal story which tells of a jackal who daubed himself with paints of many colours and then expected his companions to treat him with the respect they might give to a peacock. Some of them fell for the deception, but others were doubtful. They said to the jackal, "The Peacocks display magnificently in the gardens." He replied, "No, I cannot manifest my glory like that." Then they asked him, "Can you cry like a Peacock?" He replied, "No, I cannot." They said, "So you can't BE a Peacock: the robe of honour of the Peacock is bestowed on him from Heaven. His glory can't be claimed by earthly labourers."

At the end, Rumi compares the jackal with the Pharoah who acquired so much power and fortune that he claimed to be God.

The image of the jackal, perhaps because of its howling, is the symbol of wilderness in Persian culture. The contemporary poet, Bamdad, in his much-aclaimed *Paria*, depicts it well:

Our world is clearly visible
Let them know this
Our world is full of thorns
Snakes occupy the deserts of our world
Let those who enter our world know
Let them beware
Our world is vast and wide
Our world is full of jackals and wolves.

(D. Shahin, 1969)

STRIPED HYAENA
(Hyaena hyaena; Persian: *Kaftar*)

The hyaena inhabits most of the Iranian provinces, and is well known generally, though most abundant in the south and along the Persian Gulf. Its scavenging role is now recognised to be useful; with its powerful jaws and neck muscles it is capable of crushing the largest bones and clearing away even cattle or camel carcases. Although a timid animal, it can nevertheless appear formidable and is feared and hated by the general populace. It may weigh as much as 40 kilogrammes, living in caves and dens in the day and only emerging at night to look for carrion. In Africa, the hyaena will hunt game as well as scavenge, but there seem to be no Iranian records of it being troublesome to domestic stock. In the past, showmen used to like to demonstrate the art (?) of extracting hyaenas from their dens with their bare hands, later exhibiting them in travelling circuses, etc. This so called sport is no longer allowed. What appears to be a hyaena is depicted among the other animals on the processional frieze at Persepolis; in the past it has been mis-identified as an Okapi, which is unlikely in the extreme.

96

BEARS

(Ursidae; Persian: *Khers)*

Of the two Iranian species of bear, the B R O W N   B E A R   *(Ursus Arctos)* is the more widespread and occupies a wider range of habitats, mostly in the northern and western forests. It is probable that the Zagros Mountain Brown Bear is of Syrian origin. They look paler than the other Iranian bears, and if this supposition is correct, Iran is the only country in which they still exist.

The Persian Brown Bear is smaller than the Grizzly, but looks just as formidable. It has a reputation for attacking people and even snatching babies and children. Whatever the truth about this, the public are generally warned to keep clear of bears, especially mothers with cubs, as they can be somewhat aggressive at this time. Young bears are small at birth, weighing no more than 0.5 kilogrammes, and at this stage are extremely vulnerable. They grow rapidly and achieve an adult weight of 250 kilogrammes. Cubs can seem very attractive and in the past were often adopted as pets by people who little realised how quickly they would grow. As cubs are easily trained to perform tricks, the travelling bear with his keeper was a common sight in the not so distant past. Nowadays it is illegal to capture or keep bears. They are omnivorous as regards food and hibernate in the winter.

The B A L U C H I S T A N   B L A C K   B E A R   *(Selenarctos Thibetanus;* Persian: *Kers-e-siah)* inhabits the mountains of Baluchistan in the south-east of Iran. These mountains have a semi-tropical moist climate with permanent rivers similar to parts of the Indian sub-continent, and contain similar fauna and flora. The Baluchistan Black Bear is the same race as the Himalayan Bear, once common in suitable habitats throughout the riverine forests of south-east Iran. Destruction of the forests for agricultural settlement led to diminution of the numbers of the Black Bear to a point where it was regarded as extinct. Some were subsequently found in the Kerman and Baluchistan Mountains, but numbers are still uncertain. It is a species in urgent need of protection and re-establishment of some suitable habitat areas.

The Black Bear is smaller than the Brown Bear, with a glossy black coat, and a handsome white V-shaped mark on the lower throat, best seen when the animal stands on its hind legs. Omnivorous, it makes use of much wild fruit such as pistachio and has also been seen feeding in palm groves. Although reputed to attack domestic animals, there is little evidence to support the allegation. Some scavenging undoubtedly takes place.

Both species of bear were used by the travelling showmen, and as in Europe, the places where they put up for the night became well known; inn-signs depicting bears were not uncommonly painted by artists who also travelled the roads seeking commissions. These signs are collectors' pieces today.

In Persian folklore the bear is often referred to as "Aunt", the implication being that her looks may be benign but her embrace can be distrastrous!

WILD CATS

(Family: *Felidae*)

At least five different species of cat have been found in Iran, occupying various habitats in almost all the provinces. Some have interbred with the domestic cat and others have been domesticated locally, such as the S T E P P E   C A T   *(Felis catus)* in the western provinces. Different races of the Steppe Cat such as the E U R O P E A N   W I L D   C A T *(Felis sylvestris)* and the A F R I C A N   W I L D   C A T   *(Felis libyca)* are all of the same species and are collectively known today as *Felis catus.* The Steppe Cat is the commonest wild cat in Iran and occupies most habitats except the dry desert regions.

The J U N G L E   C A T   *(Felis chaus)* can be found in the Caspian forests and reed-beds of western Iran. A small population has been reported in the reed-beds of Hamoon in Sistan Province.

The L Y N X   *(Lynx lynx;* Persian: *Siah-goosh)* is one of the largest wild cats in Eurasia. In Iran its present habitat is confined to the higher altitudes, mainly in the foothills of some of the stonier mountains. While probably subsisting on smaller mammals such as rabbits and ground- dwelling birds, it may also be powerful enough to predate wild sheep and goats. Its Persian name means "black ears" and it is a very handsome animal with a lion-like face and a thick coat for protection in the colder climate which it favours.

The M A N U L   C A T   *(Felis manul;* Persian: *Gorbeh palas)* is a very beautiful cat with a flat face, stripes on the flanks, a spotted forehead and a short bushy tail. It is to be found in the north-eastern and eastern areas of Iran, but is very rare, and numbers are said to have declined in the breeding areas. It is now protected and numbers may be recovering somewhat.

Dry mountainous valley in Khorasan Province, typical habitat of some of the smaller cats.   Photo: E. Kahrom

The C A R A C A L (*Lynx caracal*) is the wild cat of the plains of the Central Kavir. It is agile, and a speedy runner. Adaptations such as a camouflaged coat pattern and large feet enable it to cope with desert and sandy conditions. It has been trained in the past to course rabbits and young gazelles.

The S A N D C A T (*Felis margarita;* Persian: *Gorbeh sheni*) may possibly live in the sand dunes of the Central Kavir. Its presence has not been positively confirmed, although it is known to inhabit neighbouring countries. A very small cat, it is one of the most beautiful, with large eyes and ears and feet covered in long hair for ease of movement in the sand.

All the important habitats for the wild cats of Iran are now protected, and the National Parks and Wildlife Refuges are enabling some scarce populations to survive, and even flourish.

SMALLER MAMMALS

In a huge country like Iran, with its great empty spaces and extremes of climate and vegetation cover, there are bound to be a great many mammals whose existence will be unknown to the average person. This is because it is the business of these smaller beasts to hide themselves, not only from Man, but from the countless other creatures who would be only too happy to turn them into breakfast. A number of these smaller mammals are nocturnal, and others spend much of their time, sometimes their entire lives, underground. We shall not spend too much time on this section of more or less invisible animals, except to point out that they do nevertheless form a major resource for certain predators who are able to catch them and whose own well-being is dependent on plentiful supplies of prey.

INDIAN CRESTED PORCUPINE
(*Hystrix indica*; Persian: *Tashi*)

This is the largest rodent of Iran and lives in the forests of the Caspian and similar habitats throughout the country. It can grow up to 1 metre in length and weigh some 20 kilogrammes.

BADGER

(*Meles meles*; Persian: *Rudak*)

Distributed mainly in the Caspian region and Zagros mountains.

HONEY BADGER

(*Mellivora capensis*; Persian: *Roodak-e-Assal Khour*)

A very rare animal in Iran, only occuring along the banks of the Dez and Karkhe rivers. Few observations have been made.

OTTER

(*Lutra lutra*; Persian: *Shang*)

Lives in most of the permanent rivers of Iran except in the extreme south.

WEASEL

(*Mustela nivalis*; Persian: *Rasoo*)

Lives in and around the mountains of the Central Elborz and is thought to attack small livestock at times.

MARBLED POLECAT

(*Vormela peregusna*; Persian: *Zardeh bar*)

Found in large numbers in the north-west of Iran, living in the plains and rocky hillsides.

COMMON INDIAN MONGOOSE
(*Herpestes edwardsi*; Persian: *Nams*)

Found mostly in the warm southern regions. It seems to be rather variable in coat colour.

SMALL INDIAN MONGOOSE
(*Herpestes auropunctatus*; Persian: *Nams-e-koochak*)

Found in towns and villages of the Sistan region, where they are esteemed for their vermin destroying capabilities, preying on insects, snakes and rodents.

HEDGEHOGS

There are four species found in Iran, of which the EUROPEAN HEDGEHOG (*Erinaceus europeus*; Persian: *Karposht-e-oropaie*) is found mainly in the west, while the LONG-EARED HEDGEHOG (*Hemiechinus auritus*) and BRANDT'S HEDGEHOG (*Paraechinus hypomelas*) are adapted to the dry areas of the country, the latter exhibiting considerable variation in colour, from very dark to almost white. Another species, the ETHIOPIAN HEDGEHOG (*Paraechinus aethiopicus*) has been recorded on a few occasions only in south Iran and islands in the Persian Gulf.

HAMSTERS, GERBILS, VOLES, JIRDS, JERBOAS, MICE AND RATS

There are a great many species of these families of rodent in Iran, which have adapted to the diversity of climatic conditions. They are nearly all nocturnal, burrowing animals, with the exception of the MID-DAY JIRD (*Meriones meridianus*), living in the sand-dunes of the north-east, which has worked out that noon is an unlikely time for foxes or owls to be about. Another adaptation to hot desert conditions is found in the SPINY MOUSE (*Acomys dimdiatus*); this creature has a thick, thorny skin which protects it from water loss and also from potential predators such as Blandford's Fox which shares its dessicated habitat. It also has the lizard-like ability to shed its tail if in danger.

Before the Revolution in 1978 some medical teams from France were at work in Iran investigating the possibility that some of these desert rodents were carriers of the infectious agent of Plague, *Bacillus pestis.* It is thought that the Biblical destruction of Sennacherib was brought about by the Assyrian army becoming infected by Plague, and it is related that mice gnawed the strings of their bows, so that they could have been camping in the middle of a cyclical eruption of Plague-carrying rodents of some sort.

SHREWS AND MOLES

A few SHREWS, including the PIGMY SHREW (*Suncus etruscus*), LESSER SHREW (*Sorex minutus*), HOUSE SHREW (*Suncus murinus*), BI-COLOURED SHREW (*Crocadura leucodon*), WHITE-TOOTHED SHREW (*Crocadura russula)* and WATER SHREW (*Neomys anomalus*) are mostly rather locally restricted to special habitats. The MEDITERRANEAN MOLE (*Talpa caeca*) is found in the Caspian area, and another very similar species is found in the west.

HARE

The C A P E   H A R E (*Lepus capensis*; Persian: *Khargoosh*) is found in all the habitats used by gazelles, cheetahs and foxes. Found throughout the country it is exceedingly variable, both in colour and size. It is most plentiful in the Caspian area, where too, the largest ones occur.

An animal especially adapted to the dry and saline areas of the Central Kavir is the L I T T L E   E A R T H - H A R E (*Allactagulus pumilio*), not a true hare at all, but a sort of non-jumping jerboa. A mountain species of mammal is the R U F E S C E N T   P I K A (*Ochtona rufescens*) which has the habit of making hay in the summer, then storing it in its burrows to eat in the winter.

Bowl, with hare illustration.   Photo: E. Kahrom

105

SQUIRRELS

The PERSIAN SQUIRREL (*Sciurus anomalus*; Persian: *Sanjab-e-Irani*) is a handsome animal found mostly in the oak forests of west and south-west Iran. It is reputed to aid in the propagation of the oaks by burying acorns in the ground, like its European counterparts.

In Baluchistan is found another squirrel, although it is much more plentiful in India. The PALM SQUIRREL (*Funambulus Pennanti*; Persian: *Sanjab-e-Rahrah*) lives in the Palm groves and being cryptically coloured is seldom seen, although it is admired and fed by the local people. Two ground squirrels occur, the FULVOUS GROUND SQUIRREL (*Spermophilus fulvus*) and the LONG-CLAWED GROUND SQUIRREL (*Spermohilus leptodactylus*). Both have fairly localised distributions.

BATS

There are at least 29 species of bat recorded in Iran, many of them common to Europe and other parts of Asia. The largest bat is the EGYPTIAN FRUIT BAT (*Rousettus aegypticus*) living in the south of the country where there is a plentiful supply of fruiting trees.

MARINE MAMMALS

The Caspian and Persian Gulf are the only marine habitats available to the fauna of Iran. Climatically, both are extremely warm and only species used to semi-tropical conditions are found either as residents or migrants.

BLUE WHALE
(*Sibbaldus musculus*: Persian: *Nahang-e-bozog*)

This is the largest known mammal. Solitary specimens are regularly seen in the warm waters of the Persian Gulf, as is the HUMP-BACKED WHALE (*Megaptera novaeangliae;* Persian: *Nahang-e-Goozh posht*), the latter more commonly in winter.

Humpback Whale   Photo: Aquila Photographics / A. P. Clarke

FINBACK WHALE
(*Blaenoptera physalis*; Persian: *Nahang-e-Khakestari*)

This is seen in large pods, often containing more than 100 individuals in the Gulf. There have been occasional, unconfirmed reports of sightings of other whales.

COMMON DOLPHIN
(*Delphinus delphis*; Persian: *Dolphin-e-mamooli*)

A familiar, friendly mammal commonly occuring in the shallow waters of the Gulf, and highly regarded by the human population. Several other dolphin species are known to penetrate the Gulf from the Indian Ocean at times, but they are not at all common.

DUGONG
(*Dugong dugong*; Persian: *Dugong*)

Probably occurs in Iranian waters as it is well known in the southern part of the Gulf, where it grazes on seaweeds and marine plants growing in shallow coastal regions. This grazing behaviour has given rise to the name "sea-cow". The Arabic name is *Aroosol bahr*, meaning "bride of the sea".

CASPIAN SEAL
(*Phoca Caspia*; Persian: *Phock*)

This is the only seal of this isolated sea. It spends the summer in the southern regions, but migrates north-east in the winter. Fishing interests have sometimes persecuted it.

REPTILES

(*Reptilia*)

A hot, dry country like Iran harbours a number of reptiles. Most of them are also found in neighbouring countries.

MARSH CROCODILE

(*Crocodylus palustris palustris*; Persian: *Tamsah*)

Also known as the Mugger, this animal is relatively unknown, even to most Persians. It is the same species as is found in India, Pakistan and Assam. In Iran it is found only in the Sarbaz River, and the last estimate was of 60-100 individuals. As a species it was classed as vulnerable by the Red Data Book of I.U.C.N. in 1982; the main threat being from hunters who seek its skin. In Iran it is a protected species and a survey carried out in 1970 suggested that at that period it was not in any immediate danger. Local education and establishment of protected areas were among the conservation measures proposed for the species by I.U.C.N. (1979). It can grow to 2 metres in length.

Marsh Crocodile   Photo: Aquila Photographics / K. Ghani

SNAKES

(Family: *Serpentes;* Persian: *Maar)*

There are many species of snake occupying various habitats in Iran. All snakes are feared by the average Persian, whether venomous or not. In Persian, the phrase "a colourful snake" denotes a person with a pleasant appearance but a deceitful character. The species found in the arid regions are reputed to be especially poisonous.

The most up-to-date information on Iranian snakes is contained in *The Snakes of Iran* by Mahmoud Latifi (trs. Sepideh Sajadian), published by the Society for the Study of Amphibians and Reptiles, with aid from the Smithsonian Foundation. It was originally published in Farsi in 1985.

INDIAN COBRA

(Naja naja; Persian: *Maar-e-Kobra)*

This is the best known variety of snake in Iran and it is found thoughout southern Asia and Taiwan, although there are several sub-species. They are found in and around cities and towns at the edge of the desert, and are the favourite species of Snake Charmers (*Maar Gear*). They adapt easily to captivity and can be made into pets (Giri Felix, 1983).

DAHL'S WHIP-SNAKE

(Coluber najadum; Persian: *Maar-e-sangi)*

A common species in open country and the stony areas of the southern part of Iran. It is an elusive diurnal species, a very slender snake measuring about 30-50 inches in length.

Gorgon's head, Hatra (note snakes in hair-style)

Photo: P. N. Humphreys

RACER

(Coluber ravergeiri; Persian: *Maar-e-boteh-ie)*

The Racer is found in stony, arid hilly and mountainous areas. It rarely attains more than 1 metre in length.

KHORASANI TEER SNAKE
(Psammophis lineolatus; Persian: *Maar)*

Only slightly poisonous, the venom of this snake usually causes a small swelling in Man. Inhabits desert areas, forest edge and mountains up to 1,500 metres. An extremely thin snake, usually under 1 metre long.

RAT SNAKE
(Elaphe dione; Persian: *Maar-e-Moosh Khour)*

Found in the forests of northern Iran as well as the sandy steppes and mountains, and feeds on rodents, birds, eggs and occasionally fish. A completely harmless species which makes a sound like that of a rattlesnake when disturbed. Rarely reaches 1 metre in length.

Iran has some of the BOA FAMILY *(Boidae)* within its borders. Although the family contains some very large snakes, those in Iran are fairly modest in size.

SAND BOA
(Elyx miliaris; Persian: *Boa-ye-sheni)*

Only grows to 60 centimetres. This snake lives in the sand and can bury itself very quickly to wait for lizards. It is harmless to Man.

The VIPER FAMILY *(Colubridae;* Persian: *Maar-e-abi)*, which constitutes most of the snakes in the world, has some members in Iran. They may live anywhere, but are mostly associated with watery habitats.

MONTPELLIER SNAKE
(Malapolon monspessulana; Persian: *Maar-e-dom deraz)*

Hunts small mammals and birds. Its venom is deadly for these creatures but not for Man.

EUROPEAN VIPER OR ADDER
(*Vipera berus;* Persian: *Afie;* also called *Maar-e-jaffaii)*

The Viper is common, and although not very poisonous is one of the most feared snakes. These differ in colour and grow to about 80 centimetres.

SEA SNAKES
(Family *Hydrophidae;* Persian *Maar-e-Daryaie)*

Closely related to the Cobras Sea Snakes are to be found, in the warm waters of the Persian Gulf.

HAWK-BILLED TURTLE
(Family: *Chelonians;*
Eretmochelys imbricata; Persian: *Laak Posht-e-dariayie)*

Breeds on some of the remote islands in the Persian Gulf, Although a protected animal, its eggs are dug out of the sand by local people. It ranges widely in the Indian Ocean and Pacific. Other turtles have been seen, but are not known to breed in the Gulf.

Hawk-billed turtle   Photo: Aquila Photographics / N. J. Bean

FOUR-TOED TORTOISE
(*Testudo horsefeldii*; Persian: *Laak-poshte chahar Angoshti*)

This lives around the Caspian and is found in Iran, Afghanistan and Turkestan. Largely a steppe animal, it overwinters in burrows, and re-emerges in the spring.

PART TWO

BIRDS

Iran is well blessed with birds, although many of them are migratory
and only pass through the country on their annual journeys north and
south. There are a number derived from the semi-tropical regions of
India and Africa which have successfully colonised parts of Iran. There
are others which have been introduced, such as the peacock, which
are really semi-domestic in Iran, but whose wild habitat is in the
jungles of India. There are some which have achieved a sort of
national status in legend, such as the nightingale and the owl, but are
rarely portrayed in specifically identifiable language, the colloquial
names often covering several species. In this section we shall only deal
with those species which are important from the point of view of
national perception, or are sufficiently unusual for some reason to
merit discussion. There is an urgent need for a reliable ornithological
survey of Iran in English with maps and identification illustrations.

Some 490 or so species of birds have been recorded in Iran, and
culturally they have been seen as emblems of freedom, although that
has not prevented many being caught and caged. The Persian word for
bird is *parandeh* which is derived from *par* (feather), and literally
means "flyer". As with other animals, birds have been illustrated in
artefacts from very early historical times, and it is occasionally possible
to derive a clue as to the region of origin of the artefact by identifying
the birds portrayed in it.

Although about three-quarters of Iran is dry or desert, only about
45 breeding species out of a total of 350 nationally are able to cope
with climatic and environmental difficulties of this sort of habitat.
However, habitats do vary considerably from mountain-top to swamp
as well as desert, and there are bird species occupying an ecological
niche in all of them. There are about 140 species which can be said to
be permanent residents and another 100 species which migrate within
the country during the winter. There are also a number of observations

of "accidental" occurrences, in which birds have been seen, outside their normal ranges. Doubtless there would be more if there was a greater number of knowledgeable observers working in the rural and more remote regions.

A very early ornithological work is *Nazhatol-Qolub*, written by Mamdollah-e-Mostowfi in 1342, which has given some biological insights into various real and mythical bird species as well as other creatures such as insects and bats. It is quoted at length by E. Firouz in his introduction to *The Birds of Iran* (Scott *et al*, 1975).

The most complete ornithological survey of Iran was that carried out by the great Russian traveller Zarudny at the end of the 19th Century. Unfortunately most of his papers are in Russian and still untranslated, although Buxton (1921) quotes a paper of his in French (Zarudny, 1889, *Recherches Zoologiques dans la Contrée Transcaspienne in Bull. de la Soc. Imp. Naturalistes de Moscou 133*, published, 1890). Other observers were mainly military men and diplomats passing through Persia to or from India, or on extended leave in the country. Some of them are household names in the British ornithological establishment, such as Ticehurst, Cheesman and Sir Percy Cox who organised an interesting survey of all the islands in the Persian Gulf. These people usually submitted their notes and observations to the *Journal of the Bombay Natural History Society*, a beautifully produced journal which was published until the Declaration of Independence in India, 1948. It has to be said that Persian fauna was something of a side-show compared to the very full and detailed work on the sub-continent itself; however, what sparse information we have is all the more valuable in view of the complete absence of information from elsewhere. Perhaps the most useful account of Iranian birds is that given in the monumental work of Etchcopar and Hué: *Les Oiseaux du Proche et du Moyen Orient*, Boubée, 1970, Paris. A survey of the four countries of Turkey, Iraq, Iran and Afganistan, it is lavishly illustrated with the ranges of the species delineated for each country. It is, although in one volume, far too big to be used as a travelling guide, and is now difficult to obtain. Jervis Read (1977) produced a useful account of past literature and a sweeping summary of bird life in Iran in general, but there has been some serious ornithological work done since then, and we have endeavoured to take account of it in the text.

The sheer number of bird species has made it difficult to divide the text up; we have therefore enumerated them more or less into related groups, and have not attempted to emulate a standard ornithology. Where possible, we have added the Persian perceptions and legends about some species. We have also been able to add some contemporary and early illustrations of some of them. Although Persians enjoy field sports, there is not the wholesale destruction of birds in Iran that is met with in other countries, such as Italy, Cyprus and the Lebanon, and a number of species are traditionally revered, including the Stork, Roller and Nightingale. The present Islamic Government of Iran pursues an enlightened conservation policy: for instance, all birds of prey are protected rigidly, there are some 60 "Protected Areas" where no shooting is allowed (with certain specified exceptions) and certain species are added to the "endangered list" if it is thought that populations are declining. The Department of Environmental Conservation has about 3,000 Game Guards working for it who have powers of arrest. Gun licences are expensive, and shooting expeditions require an additional licence. Most shooting is done in the winter in the southern Caspian region, where the vast flocks of wildfowl have been traditionally hunted. Penalties are heavy for infringement of the conservation laws.

NIGHTINGALE

(Luscinia megarhynchos; Persian: *Bolbol)*

The Nightingale comprises three species: N I G H T I N G A L E *(Luscinia megarhynchos);* T H R U S H   N I G H T I N G A L E *(Luscinia luscinia);* and W H I T E - E A R E D   B U L B U L *(Pycnonotus leucotis).* They are all three brown birds with melodious songs. The Thrush Nightingale is the most widely distributed and can be found at all seasons, while the Nightingale is the familiar bird of Europe and is migratory, nesting mainly in the northern and western provinces of Iran. The other (true) bulbul is a sub-tropical visitor, as its Persian name *Bolbol khorma (Date Bulbul)* implies.

Palmgrove in Khoramshahr, southern Iran. Habitat of the Bulbul. Photo: E. Kahrom

A great deal of Persian poetry and folklore has to do with the relationship of the Nightingale and the rose. Like the confectionery in the Middle East, much of it is over sweet and grossly sentimental; however, generally speaking, the Nightingale is a bird of good omen and happiness.

RAPTORS

OSPREY

(*Pandion halietus*; Persian: *Oghab-e-Mahigeir*)

Osprey may be found along the coasts of the Persian Gulf and Caspian Sea. They breed in both regions and are relatively common, providing a magnificent spectacle whether perching in dead trees or diving to catch fish. It is uncertain that they breed all round the Gulf, a small population certainly does near Bandar-e-Bushir.

KITES

(*Milvus*)

Two species of Kite breed in Iran.

The R E D   K I T E (*Milvus milvus*; Persian: *Kur kur-e-Manaie*) breeds only in a small area of northern Azerbaijan and a few winter along the

121

southern coasts of the Caspian Sea. The species does not occur elsewhere in Iran.

The B L A C K   K I T E (*Milvus migrans*; Persian: *Kur kur*) is much more plentiful and breeds almost throughout Iran. Those breeding round the Caspian coast and the southern half of Iran remain on their breeding grounds throughout the year. They are seen in flocks, often at some altitude, flying over towns and rubbish tips or gathering around carcases. They are tree nesters and may use the nests of other species, such as crows, on occasion.

HAWKS

(Persian: *Ghoush*)

The G O S H A W K (*Accipiter gentilis*; Persian: *Tarlan*) is found only in northern Iran and occupies the same sort of habitats as the Red Kite. They breed in small numbers and a few are found wintering in Fars and Baluchistan. It is not clear whether these are some of the same group which breeds in the north. They are fast and agile flyers and are adapted to hunting in the dense forests of their breeding areas.

The L E V A N T   S P A R R O W - H A W K (*Accipiter brevipes*; Persian: *Peighou*) breeds in some areas of the north and north-west, and is also a woodland bird, but in the winter seems to prefer more open ground with scattered bushes and trees. It is not common, and is restricted to a small part of the country, although more birds may pass through on migration, and some have been reported from Baluchistan in the south-east.

SHIKRA (*Accipter badius*; Persian: *Peigho-ye-kochak*) means "the liitle sparrow-hawk", the male being a smaller version of the Levant Sparrow-Hawk. This bird has an interesting distribution, being present and only breeding in the summer in the south and eastern parts of the Caspian coast, and also the provinces of Khorassan and Kerman. It is a breeding resident in Baluchistan and a winter visitor to the south-east corner of Iran. The favourite habitat is areas with scattered trees and open farmland. It is fairly common in the summer in the eastern provinces.

Cup, overglaze painted, Rayy, 13th Century, depicting a typical scene of the chase.   Photo: E. Kahrom

123

SPARROW-HAWK
(*Accipiter nisus*; Persian: *Gherghi*)

The Sparrow-Hawk is the commonest hawk in Iran, its breeding habitat being similar to that of the Levant Sparrow-Hawk. The breeding habitats are occupied in winter, although there is also dispersion to most other parts of the country except Sistan and Baluchistan. The bird is well known to Persians and the word *Gherghi* is synonymous with speed, agility, quick thinking and manoeuvrability. It is common in all seasons and is also partially migratory.

HARRIER
(Persian: *Circus*)

These are large to medium size hawks which hunt by quartering the area in which they are likely to find prey. They have a characteristic buoyant flight and when a small mammal or bird is perceived, they drop directly onto it. They are usually di-morphic, the females larger than the males. All species listed below are migratory.

HEN HARRIER
(*Circus cyaneus*; Persian: *Songhor-e-Khahestari*)

The commonest Persian harrier, it is seen over a variety of habitats, especially in the winter.

PALLID HARRIER
(Circus macrourus; Persian: *Songhor-e-Sephid)*

Its Persian name means "white" and it migrates throughout the country, apart from the north-west, which has no record of its presence. It is possible that there is a small breeding population in the north-east, but this requires confirmation.

MONTAGU'S HARRIER
(Circus pygargus; Persian: *Songhar-e-Gandomzar)*

The Persians call this the "wheat-farm harrier", which describes a prefered habitat. It breeds in very small numbers, in the north-west, although stray individuals are seen elsewhere on migration.

MARSH HARRIER
(Circus; Persian: *Songhor-e-talabi)*

This fine bird breeds in the marshes of north-west Iran, and the most suitable marshes there support a pair or more. It is partly migratory, some of the northern breeding birds spending the winter in the south. A small group is also known to breed at Lake Hamoon, in the east. This is an isolated lake, partly in Afghanistan in fact, which acts as a haven for all manner of water birds, such as avocets, terns, water rail, etc. The surrounding country is very dry, giving increased importance to the only sizeable body of water in a large region

BUZZARDS

(*Buteo*; Persian: *Sargapeh* ho)

HONEY BUZZARD
(*Pernis apivorus*; Persian: *Sargapeh-e-zangali*)

To the Persians this is the "Forest Buzzard", as the bird confines itself
to a narrow strip of the Caspian forests south of the Caspian Sea and
Azarbaijan; the same areas inhabited by Red Kites and Goshawks. It
only breeds in these districts and is usually absent in winter. Iran is
used as a migration route by a small number of birds of this species.

ROUGH-LEGGED BUZZARD
(*Buteo lagopus*; Persian: *Sargarpeh-e-Parpa*)

Only a few individuals are known to winter in the Caspian area and
the eastern Turkmen plains. They are uncommon in Iran and probably
do not breed there. Some occasional occurrences have been reported
in other northern provinces.

COMMON BUZZARD
(*Buteo buteo*; Persian: *Sargarpeh*)

Local in the Caspian region, breeding there and resident in the winter.
The species has also been found in large numbers in other parts of
northern Iran, usually attracted by carcases. Rabbits and rodents may
be predated by them. A sub-species (*B.p. vulpinus*) also winters in Iran,

126

although breedings to the north of the country. There are plumage differences between the two sub-species, although this a very variable species anyway.

LONG-LEGGED BUZZARD
(*Buteo rufinus*; Persian: *Sargarpeh-e-Paboland*)

The commonest Iranian buzzard, breeding in almost all the northern provinces and resident there during the winter. It is not known to breed in the south, but large numbers are present in the winter. The preferred habitats of this species are plains, drylands and sometimes mountainous areas.

WHITE-EYED BUZZARD
(*Butastur teesa*; Persian: *Sargapeh-e-Cheshm sephid*)

This is a small buzzard confined to the south-eastern corner of Iran, and not seen elsewhere. It both breeds and is resident in this locality, and can be found in woodland, open spaces and agricultural land. Tree nesters, they can sometimes be seen in small groups.

EAGLE

(Persian: *Oghab*)

The Eagle has long been a symbolic bird for the Iranians, and many other nations, too. The avian equivalent of lions, they have appeared in a great many artefacts, from legionary standards to statuary on important buildings. Hybrids between lions and eagles, "griffins", have been favourite confections, symbolically representing swiftness and strength.

In Persian literature there are of course many eagle stories. An old one tells of an eagle brought down from his high station in the sky by an arrow, which on close inspection is found to be flighted by an eagle's feather.

The piercing gaze of the eagle, its majesty in flight and swift dispatch of prey have also been remarked upon by poets and writers through the ages. A contemporary poet, M. Sheibani, makes his dying eagle wish to be buried in the clouds instead of the damp ground; and another, K. Golesorki, writes:

> In me there is a reformed eagle
> Who has never talked about tiredness
> Who has never said "yes",
> Never ask me to land.
>
> *(D. Shahin 1970)*

At least nine species of eagle have been reported in Iran, and have been remarked upon by travellers, particularly in the mountainous parts of the country.

BOOTED EAGLE
(*Hieraaetus pennatus*; Persian: *Oghabe parpa*)

This is the commonest of the eagles in the north of Iran. It breeds in the Caspian Forests, and can often be seen flying among the trees, manoeuvring themselves with great agility. There appears to be migration and passage through Iran during the summer, when numbers increase. This eagle is primarily a forest species and is rarely found in open areas.

BONNELLI'S EAGLE
(*Hieraaetus fasciatus*; Persian: *Oghabe do barodar*)

This is another common eagle, and can be seen almost anywhere in Iran except at very high altitudes, and in the north-western corner. It is a formidable hunter and extremely agile flyer. Although they prefer rocky mountains and crags for nesting and perching, during winter they hunt in more open country, capturing rodents, and other small mammals and birds.

TAWNY EAGLE
(*Hieraaetus nipalensis*; Persian: *Oghabe dashti*)

Also known as the Steppe Eagle, this bird breeds in south-east Iran and winters in the south-west. It is a bird of open spaces and vast plains, and often hunts by low level gliding, preying on small mammals, snakes, frogs, etc.

SPOTTED EAGLE
(*Aquila clanga*; Persian: *Oghab-e-Talabie*)

The Persian name denotes "Marsh Eagle" which is descriptive of its preferred habitat, i.e. areas with trees near lakes or rivers, etc. It breeds in the south Caspian area in trees or bushes and is usually resident. In winter, it can be seen almost anywhere except the southern districts.

LESSER SPOTTED EAGLE
(*Aquila pomarina*; Persian: *Oghabe zangali*)

This is a smaller version of the Spotted Eagle, which sometimes hovers. It breeds in the rich, forested hills and mountains of north-west Iran, some 240,000 hectares of which is now protected.

WHITE-TAILED EAGLE
(*Haliaeetus albicilla*; Persian: *Oghab-e-Daryaee-Dom-sephid*)

The Latin, Persian and English names are synonomous in meaning. The bird breeds in large numbers in the south Caspian area, nesting on cliffs, rocks, trees and even on the ground near water. It is primarily a fish-eating eagle and may submerge entirely when fishing, its powerful wing-beats enabling it to carry off even large fish at times. In winter it is found in suitable habitats anywhere in Iran and along the Persian Gulf.

IMPERIAL EAGLE
(*Aquila heliaca*; Persian: *Oghab-e-Shahi*)

A very large eagle residing in remote plains and marshes, building conspicuous nests in tall trees and adding to them from year to year. A small group nests in the southern Caspian region and during the winter wandering individuals can be seen in many parts of northern Iran.

GOLDEN EAGLE
(*Aquila chrysaetos;* Persian: *Oghab-e-Talaie*)

This magnificent bird breeds in the north and west of Iran and usually winters in its breeding areas, where it may be quite plentiful. Crags and rocky mountains and occasional coastal cliffs and the tops of trees are used as nesting sites. As a bird of prey it is formidable, flying close to the ground and attacking grouse, hares, fawns, etc., at close range.

Golden Eagle   Photo: the late H. R. Biat

SHORT-TOED EAGLE
(*Circaetus gallicus*; Persian: *Oghab-e-markour*)

The alternative English name, "Snake-eating Eagle", is the same as the Persian. The bird feeds mainly on reptiles and frogs, and can often be seen with prey dangling from its talons as it flies. There are two colour phases of this bird, light and dark, which breeds along the Persian Gulf and can be found where snakes and reptiles abound in many places in Iran. It is a tree nester.

FALCONS

(*Falconidae*; Persian: *Shahin* or *baz-e-shekari* = hunting hawk)

At least 10 members of this family are known to occur in Iran, occupying a variety of habitats.

SAKER FALCON
(*Falco cherrug*; Persian: *Balaban*)

This is one of the commonest Iranian falcons, nesting in the north and central provinces in fair numbers, the population increasing in the winter with the addition of migrants from elsewhere. It is a brave and determined hunter, hence a favourite falconry species. Its favoured habitat is open country with semi-desert conditions.

PEREGRINE FALCON
(*Falco peregrinus*; Persian: *Bahri*)

This bird breeds in small numbers in the north of the country, with increased numbers seen throughout Iran in winter. A popular falconer's bird, mainly because of its spectacular method of hunting, it nests on crags and rocky projections, but hunts in more open country as a rule.

BARBARY FALCON
(*Falco pelgrinoides*; Persian: *Shahin*)

Said by some to be a race of the Peregrine Falcon, this is the most widely known bird of prey in Iran. The name is derived from the word *shah* and denotes nobility and grace. It is common, though somewhat local in distribution; and is a resident, breeding in upland areas and dispersing over the plains in winter.

LANNER FALCON
(*Falco biarmicus*; Persian: *Latin*)

This is a rare species and appears to breed only on some small islands of Rezaieh Lake in the north-west. A very illusive bird, it is infrequently seen.

HOBBY
(*Falco subbuteo*; Persian: *Leil*)

The Hobby breeds in the northern and south-western provinces. The usual habitat consists of open country with scattered trees, but it can also be found in the tops of tall cypresses surrounding urban gardens, such as the Bagh-e-fin near Kashan. It preys on small birds and large insects, such as dragon-flies, and is often active at dusk in pursuit of them.

MERLIN
(*Falco columbarius*; Persian: *Tromtay*)

This little falcon breeds in northern Europe, but can be found in Iran in winter, especially in the northern provinces, often quite plentifully.

RED-FOOTED FALCON
(*Falco vespertinus*; Persian: *Tromtay-e-Pa sorkh*)

A beautiful but rare falcon, it is highly gregarious, and is always found in groups. It inhabits the edge of forests, plains and farmland. There have been no recent observations.

LESSER KESTREL
(*Falco naumanni*; Persian: *Delijeh-e-couchak*)

Another gregarious bird, but quite common, colonising cliffs and hunting over fields and plains.

Lesser Kestrel   Photo: Aquila Photographics / Hanne & Jens Eriksen

K E S T R E L
(*Falco tinnunculus*; Persian: *Delijeh*)

The commonest falcon, it breeds in most situations where it can find its prey of voles and mice, and is therefore widely distributed.

VULTURES

(Persian: *Karkas*)

Iran has five breeding species of vultures, and they are a common sight, sailing in the intense blue of the Persian sky, ever watchful for signs of death below. They are also referred to as "carcase eaters".

EGYPTIAN VULTURE
(*Neophron perccnopterus*; Persian: *Karkas*)

The Egyptian Vulture seems to occupy an inferior position in vulture society, and is usually the last to feed on a carcase where other vultures have gathered. Although not normally gregarious, several will gather at one carcase. The species has now learned to scavenge on the rubbish tips near villages, although generally avoiding cities and larger towns. It nests among rocks, and is resident in the south of the country, where, in the summer, large numbers can be seen.

BLACK VULTURE
(*Aegypius monachus*; Persian: *Dal-e-siah*)

A year-round resident, it is fairly common. The Persian name is derived from the wedge-shaped tail (*dal*) which signifies the letter D. À rather solitary bird, it nests in trees and on crags and is a bird of the mountains and great plains.

GRIFFON VULTURE
(*Gyps fulvus*; Persian: *Dal*)

A gregarious bird which nests with others on cliffs and in caves. It is a resident, but has not been found along the southern shores of the Caspian Sea, probably because of the more intensive nature of the agriculture in this area and relatively high density of the human population. Also, carcases are not usually left to lie as in more remote areas.

Griffon Vulture   Photo: late H. R. Biat

WHITE-BACKED VULTURE
(*Pseudogyps bengalenis*; Persian: *Dal-e-Posht sefid*)

Of Indian origin, this vulture breeds only in the south-east corner of Iran. It seems to be generally a lowland bird, gregarious and resident in its breeding area. Although few in numbers, it does not appear threatened or endangered.

BEARDED VULTURE
(*Gypaetus barbatus*; Persian: *Homa*)

This was thought to be a bird of good omen – so much so that if someone by some strange chance had one alight on his head, he was

137

immediately crowned king! Needless to say, such coronations were extremely rare. It is a solitary bird, not often seen at carcases with other vultures. Its shape and general behaviour is more like that of a bird of prey. It nests on cliffs and in small caves in its remote mountainous habitat, is relatively abundant in such areas, but seems to avoid the very dry regions of the Central Desert and eastern drylands. There is a small population breeding in the Mokran Mountains in the same region occupied by the White-backed Vulture. It feeds much on the bone marrow from larger carcases such as those of Ibex and Wild Sheep, and drops the bones from a great height to break them, also preying on tortoises in this manner.

Bearded Vulture (Lammegeir)   Illustration: E. Kahrom

Apart from the above species, vultures are always associated with death in Persian culture, their cry being a reminder of Man's inevitable fate. In the 18th and 19th centuries, the Zoroastrians built numerous "Towers of Silence" on which they exposed their dead, until, in modern times, the practice was prohibited for sanitary considerations. Some of these structures can still be seen, especially in the Kerman area; but even without this dietary supplement, vultures can still be seen wheeling in the immense skies above Iran.

SWANS, GEESE AND DUCKS

(Family: *Anatidae*)

The members of this family are widely dispersed in Iran in suitable habitats, and enjoy a favourable image among the people on account of beauty and/or usefulness. The southern Caspian region attracts great numbers of wildfowl in the winter and spring, the area being used both as a wintering ground and port-of-call for migratory species. A few of the most important and interesting species are discussed below.

MUTE SWAN
(*Cygnus olor*; Persian: *Gooye-gong*)

This is the commonest species, but breeding only very locally, possibly in Sistan. Flocks have been seen in Fars in the past but nowadays most observations are from the southern Caspian Sea, mainly in hard weather when they become more numerous.

WHOOPER SWAN
(*Cygnus cygnus*; Persian: *Ghooye-faryad kesh*)

A wintering species in the Caspian where the noisy V-formations flying overhead are one of the most spectacular sights in the area. Wandering individuals have also been seen in the wetlands of Fars and Sistan.

BEWICK'S SWAN
(*Cygnus bewickii*; Persian: *Ghooye-kouchak*)

This is the rarest swan in Iran. Small parties winter in the Caspian, and occasionally are seen on the great plains surrounding the Lake Rezaieh National Park, along with other waterfowl.

GEESE
(*Anser*; Persian: *Ghaz*)

The RED-BREASTED GOOSE (*Anser ruficollis*) is the rarest and most handsome of the species of geese recorded as wintering in Iran. Others include GREY-LAG (*Anser anser*), WHITE-FRONTED (*Anser albifrons*) and LESSER WHITE-FRONTED (*Anser erythriopus*). These winter in the Caspian region, sometimes in immense flocks, but only the Grey-lag is known to breed in Azarbijan province.

THE GREATER FLAMINGO

(*Phoenicopterus ruber,* Persian: *Morgh-e-Husseini*)

The only flamingo to occur in Iran, and breeds on some of the small islands of Lake Rezaieh. The saline waters encourage the crustacea on which the flamingoes feed and the uninhabited islands which are out of bounds to the public provide the necessary security. The Persian name denotes the "Blood of the Prophet Hussein", a reference to the red colouration of the plumage. Another name translates as "firebird". A large number of birds winters in Fars and Kusistan, and it is thought that some may breed in Kusistan.

Lake Parishan in Fars. The flamingoes can be seen as a strip of light at the far edge of the water.   Photo: E. Kahrom

141

STORKS

(Family *Ciconiidae* Persian: *Lak lak*)

The White Stork (*Ciconia ciconia*; Persian: *Lak-lak-e-sephid*) is the commonest and best known species of stork in Iran. As in other parts of its range, it is regarded with affection by the human population and is popularly known as *Haji lak-lak* because of its presumed pilgrimage to Mecca every year, although in fact a small population winters in Kusistan province. The arrival of the storks is a sign that winter is passing. Nesting as it does on roofs and even antique columns, it is familiar to most Persians, who protect the nests from disturbance.

Pasargidae. Stork's nest on sole remaining column.　　Photo: P. N. Humphreys

BLACK STORK
(*Ciconia nigra*; Persian: *Lak-lak-e-siah*)

This bird is not so common or well known. Generally a tree nester, it breeds in the northern provinces. A few winter in Fars and the bird is sometimes seen on migration.

In Iran, as elsewhere in the Middle East, drainage and intensive modes of agriculture have reduced the feeding grounds of the Stork, which relies to a great extent on amphibians and fish for food, but nevertheless does eat snakes, lizards and small mammals, as well as feeding extensively on swarms of locusts when these appear. Because of the almost total failure of government action to intensify agriculture in Iran (McLachlan, 1988), this malign effect is perhaps not quite so marked as elsewhere, but the increased cultivation of rice around Rasht and the southern Caspian region, with the modern unrestricted use of pesticides, must give rise to concern about the welfare of these useful and beautiful birds.

BUSTARDS

(Family *Otidae*; Persian: *Houbarreh*)

Iran has three breeding species of these spectacular, shy, game birds. The wide open spaces of Iran are particularly suited to them and, along with the Gazelle, they have been esteemed as objects of the chase for centuries.

GREAT BUSTARD
(*Otis tarda*; Persian: *Mish Morgh*)

Two populations of Great Bustards are known in Iran. One group breeds on the vast rolling plains in the west, and appears to be resident. Another breeds on the plains of the former Soviet Union and winters in Iran. Although protected by law, there is reason to believe that agricultural intensification may have damaged their habitats. Another problem is that the breeding areas of the most westerly population coincided with the battleground of the eight-year long Iraq/Iran War. It is not known how the bustards survived this conflagration, or, indeed, if they did at all.

LITTLE BUSTARD
(*Otis tetrax*; Persian: *Zanguleh Ball*)

This species breeds in the south-east of Iran in small numbers, augmented by birds migrating from the north in winter.

HOUBARA BUSTARD
(*Chlamydotis undulata*; Persian: *Houbarreh*)

This is the bird that most Persians think of when Bustards are discussed. It has long been a favourite target species for falconers. It breeds on the plains of the south-east, and is partly migratory within or near the breeding grounds.

OWLS

(Family *Strigidae*; Persian: *Joghd*)

Owls are not good news to the average Persian. As in many other parts of the world, they are seen as birds of ill omen – the only living creatures that are likely to profit from war and devastation. This is possibly because ruined buildings often make ideal nesting sites for them. Making an enemy's city a "habitation for owls" is an old Biblical threat, and their crepuscular habits and eerie calls all accentuate the gloomy image. Certain species do have a reputation for wisdom, as does the Little Owl (*Athene noctua*) in Europe or the Scops Owl (*Otus scops*) in Iran; here it is known as the "bird of righteousness", its monotonous call being a reminder of death and the day of judgement.

Eagle Owl

Photo: Aquila Photographics / R. Maier

Eleven species of owl have been recorded in Iran. Some are indigenous and others rare visitors. Below is a brief account of some of the species.

EAGLE OWL
(*Bubo bubo*; Persian: *Shah boof*)

This immense owl is common. It breeds throughout the country, and is a fairly stationary resident. Because of its size it can cope with large prey, such as rabbits. A solitary bird, it will hold its territory for years.

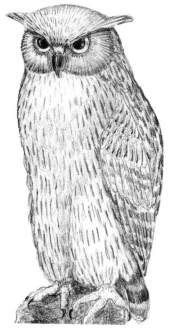

BROWN FISH OWL
(*Ketupa zeylonensis*; Persian: *Jogh-e-Mahi Khar*)

This species is found in forests near water. This means that it is fairly localised, and being very illusive it is hard to be sure of the population status. It is known to breed in the marshes of western Kusistan.

Brown Fish Owl
Illustration: Susan Jane Street

SCOPS OWL
(*Otus scops;* Persian: *Morgh-e-Haq*)

This bird is well known in Iran and breeds throughout the country. In the south the Striated Scops Owl *(Otus brucei)* is also resident locally.

The other owls are only found in small numbers in appropriate habitats, and there is some seasonal migration about the country.

PARTRIDGES AND PHEASANTS

(*Phasianidae*; Persian: *Garghavol*)

This family has seven members occurring in Iran.

CASPIAN SNOWCOCK
(*Tetragallus caspius;* Persian: *Kabk-e-Dari*)

This is a rare resident of the snowy peaks of the Elborz and Zagros mountains, with some found in Azerbayjan. It is hardly ever found below 3,500 metres altitude and appears to be a fairly solitary bird, not moving far from its territory, even in winter.

SEE-SEE PARTRIDGE
(*Ammoperdix griseogularis*; Persian: *Teyhoo*)

Essentially a desert bird, cryptically coloured. It is very common, and is found almost everywhere except the northernmost regions.

BLACK PARTRIDGE OR FRANCOLIN
(*Francolinus francolinus*; Persian: *Doraj*)

Another common species, especially in the southern provinces, but also breeds in Azerbaijan and south of the Caspian. Its preferred habitat is grassland, tamarisk and marshes.

GREY PARTRIDGE
(*Francolinus pondicerianus*; Persian: *Girofty*)

Found only in the south-east, in Sistan and Baluchistan, where it is resident and locally abundant. It favours dry land with tamarisk and bush, especially along river banks.

ROCK PARTRIDGE
(*Alectoris Chukar*)

Prefers fairly bare and broken ground. A noisy bird and used for a form of cock-fighting at times. There are a number sub-species common through Balkans and orient generally, which has been a favourite subjects for artists.

Rock Partridge, Kavir National Park.

Photo: H. R. Biat

COMMON PARTRIDGE
(*Perdix perdix*; Persian: *Kabk-e-cheel*)

In contrast to the last species, this one is only found in the north-west, in fairly small numbers, being a resident in cultivated farmland and pasture, as it is elsewhere in its range.

QUAIL
(*Coturnix coturnix*; Persian: *Belderchin*)

This is the Biblical Quail which irrupted in vast numbers in the Siniai Peninsula and fed the wandering Israelites for a time. It is common in Iran on steppes, grasslands and farmland, and is evidently a resident. The flocks may be very large on occasion.

PHEASANT
(*Phasianus colchicus*; Persian: *Gharghavol*)

There are a number of sub-species and races of this colourful bird in Iran, all of them resident. It is an indigenous bird and occupies grassland and woodland habitats, particularly in the north. When cover is sparse, it prefers to run and hide rather than to fly.

CRANES

(Family: *Gruidae*)

COMMON CRANE
(*Grus grus*; Persian: *Dorna*)

A very prominent and handsome species found in the marshlands of Iran in winter. Although not breeding in Iran, its arrival in large, noisy flocks in the Caspian area signals the arrival of the winter season. It disperses througout Iran to suitable sites and is familiar to most people.

SIBERIAN CRANE
(*Grus leucogeranus*; Persian: *Dorna-ye-sephid*)

This magnificent white bird was formerly a regular visitor to the Caspian marshlands, but for a long time there was no valid report of the species wintering in Iran. Recently, very small numbers have been seen once again, and attempts have been made to propagate them by captive breeding and reintroduction into the wintering areas. It is not known if this project achieved any success. Possibly, protection on their Siberian breeding grounds has led to a small increase in numbers.

Siberian Crane   Photo: Aquila Photographics / K. Ghaemi

DEMOISELLE CRANE
(*Anthrpoides virgo*; Persian: *Dorna-te-Kouchak*)

This bird travels through Iran on migration, and has been seen only in very small numbers in recent years.

SWIFTS

(Family: *Apodidae*)

Of the four species of swift found in Iran in summer, only the PALLID SWIFT (*Apus pallidus*; Persian: *Bad khorak-e-doodi*) appears to be resident. It only occurs along the coasts of the Persian Gulf and south-west corner of the country, where it is quite common. The COMMON SWIFT (*Apus apus*; Persian: *Bad Khorak-e-Mamooli*) is a well loved visitor to towns and cities where its familiar screaming parties are well known. The gregarious LITTLE SWIFT (*Apus affinus*) and the ALPINE SWIFT (*Apus melba*) also occur, the latter mostly in mountainous districts and less in towns.

HOOPOES

(Family *Upupidae*; Persian: *Hod-hod*)

The Hoopoe (*Upupa epops*) is a summer visitor to Iran and breeds widely. In popular belief its crest derives from the crown of Solomon, and it is generally revered. Its more prosaic name, *Shaneh*, translates as "comb on head", which is more literal but much duller.

ROLLERS

(Family Coraciidae)

THE ROLLER
(*Coracias garrulus*; Persian: *Sabz-e-ghaba*)

The brilliantly plumaged Roller is a familiar bird to the Persians, and its name translates literally as "green cloak". The colour is of great significance to Moslems as the sign of the Prophet, evidenced by the green turbans of the clergy. The bird is also renowned for its spectacular display. A highly visible bird, it perches on telegraph posts and such along the roads, waiting for insects or small lizards, etc., to appear on the ground below. As its Latin name suggests, it is a noisy bird, although not normally gregarious. A summer visitor, it breeds in the northern three-quarters of the country, being replaced by the Indian Roller (*Coracias bengalensis*) in the south.

SWALLOWS AND MARTINS

(Family: *Hirundinidae*)

These are harbingers of spring in Iran as elsewhere, and their arrival from Africa is always welcome.

SAND MARTIN
(*Riparia riparia*; Persian: *Chelcheleh-e-Roudkhanie*)

Breeds in the north and west of the country, though it can be seen on migration throughout the country.

Sand Martins on migration.　　　　　Photo: Aquila Photographics / M. C. Wilkes

CRAG MARTIN
(*Hirundo rupestris*; Persian: *Chelcheleh-e-Kouhi*)

The Crag Martin is associated with mountainous areas, but is more widely distributed, often building with the House Martins (*Delichon*

Urbica; Persian: *Chelcheleh-e-Domgah sephid*), which nest in large numbers in some of the towns.

PALE CRAG MARTIN
(*Hirundo obsoleta*; Persian: *Chelcheleh-e-Biabanie*)

The Pale Crag Martin is the lowland version of the Crag Martin, occurring at lower altitudes and often near bodies of freshwater. They are rarely seen in towns, and are only partly migratory, spending the winter in the Persian Gulf region.

SWALLOW
(*Hirundo rustica*; Persian: *Parastoo*)

The swallow breeds throughout the country and nests in buildings and sheds in villages and on farms, where they are always very welcome and protected. Although migratory, it is thought that a small group of swallows may spend the winter in the south-east corner of the country.

RED-RUMPED SWALLOW
(*Hirundo daurica*; Persian: *Parastoo-ye-domgah soorati*)

This bird is more associated with towns, bridges and other man-made structures, breeding mostly in the south-western provinces, Luristan, Fars and Kerman.

CROWS

(Family: *Corvidae*)

This successful group of birds is represented by 11 species in Iran. They are all omnivorous and thus will take carrion, fruit and small creatures as food.

The Persian word for "crow", *kalagh*, implies an ugly bird (or person!) without any obvious talent, or at best a malign one. The poet Saadi says, "It is not strange if the presence of the Raven makes the Nightingale quiet." The Crow is also supposed to be long-lived and proverbially it is said that "Talent shortens the life of the Nightingale but its absence makes life longer for the Crow." The bird has a special place in children's stories, the noisy, evening flocks being familiar to them as they come home from school.

JAY
(*Garrulous glandarius*; Persian: *Zi-zagh*)

This noisy, colourful bird breeds in the forests of the north and north-west, and appears to be a resident.

PLESKE'S GROUND JAY
(*Podesces pleskei*; Persian: *Zaghe-boor*)

This is totally unlike the other corvids, spending most of its time on the ground. It is a resident of the plains and deserts of central Iran.

156

MAGPIE
(*Pica pica*; Persian: *Zaghi*)

A common resident, it is however absent from the south-east and northern parts of the Persian Gulf.

CHOUGH
(*Pyrrhocorax pyrrhocorax*; Persian: *Zagh-e-nok sorkh*)

The Red-billed Chough is well adapted to living in such a mountainous country as Iran, and is frequently seen in quite large flocks wheeling and making a clamour, along crags and ravines. Its close relative, with a yellow bill, is the Alpine Chough (*Pyrrhocorax graculus*; Persian: *Zagh-e-nok zand*) which is found only in the northern provinces on the high peaks in the breeding season, but descends to lower altitudes in the winter.

JACKDAW
(*Corvus monedula*; Persian: *Kalagh-e-gardan boor*)

This bird is only resident in the north, where it has adapted to town life. There are signs of an expansion of the breeding population in the north-east, and wintering birds move more to the south, but never beyond the central provinces, and it is not known in the south at all.

HOODED CROW

(*Corvus corone cornix*; Persian: *Kalagh-e-Ablagh*)

The Hooded Crow is the northern and eastern variety of the black crow of Europe, and is both common and familiar. Two other sub-species are met in Iran, with plumage variations that make it look a totally different bird; these seem to be just local variations and the species may interbreed if their ranges merge.

Hooded Crow   Photo: Aquila Photographics / Mike Lane

HOUSE CROW

(*Corvus splendens*; Persian: *Kalagh-e-Hendi*)

A smaller version of the Hooded Crow, it is localised in Iran to the Persian Gulf and Karg Island. It is thought to be a species introduced from the east, although it could be accounted for by natural expansion at some time in the past.

R O O K
(*Corvus frugilegus*; Persian: *Khalagh-e-siah*)

Breeds in large numbers in the northern provinces, as it does in adjacent Turkey, and migrates southwards in winter.

R A V E N
(*Corvus corax*; Persian: *Ghorab*)

A resident, breeding throughout Iran, with the exception of the southeast provinces where it is replaced by the slightly smaller Brown-necked Raven (*Corvus ruficollis*), which is more adapted to desert conditions.

THRUSHES

(*Turdidae*; Persian: *Toukay*)

B L A C K - T H R O A T E D T H R U S H
(*Turdus ruficollis* Persian: *Toukay-e-galoo siah*)

Migrant, only met with on plain and farmland in winter.

FIELDFARE
(*Turdus pilaris*; Persian: *Toukay-e-Posht Balooti*)

Another wintering migrant from the north, quite well known in parts of the northern provinces, and sometimes penetrating as far as Fars and Kusistan.

RING OUSEL
(*Turdus torquata*; Persian: *Touka-ye-Toughi*)

This handsome thrush breeds in the mountains and hills of the north, nesting where there is plenty of cover, often near springs and rivers. Wintering birds have been seen as far south as Kusistan, and both breeding and wintering birds occur in large numbers.

BLACKBIRD
(*Turdus merula*; Persian: *Toukay-ye-siah*)

The commonest thrush in the region, associated with gardens, woodland and areas with dense vegetation. It breeds in the northern and western areas, wintering in most districts except the extreme south-east.

REDWING
(*Turdus iliacus*; Persian: *Toukay-ye-ball sorkh*)

Winters in the northern provinces, and only occasionally have small numbers been found elsewhere.

Redwing   Photo: Aquila Photographics / Nigel Ede

SONG THRUSH
(*Turdus philomelos*; Persian: *Toukay-ye-baghi*)

As its Persian name implies, this is the thrush of gardens and parks, and is popular and familiar. It breeds only in very small numbers in the Caspian area, but is met with all over Iran in the winter.

MISTLE TRUSH
(*Turdus viscivorus*; Persian: *Toukay-ye-bosorg*)

A breeder in the north and west, occupying roughly the same habitat as the Song Thrush, frequenting more open land after the breeding season.

BLUE ROCK THRUSH
(*Monticula solitarius*; Persian: *Toukay banash*).

This beautiful singer breeds in the north of Iran, in much the same habitat as the Ring Ousel, and moves to the Gulf area in the winter.

CHATS

WHEATEAR
(*Oenanthe*; Persian: *Chek chek*)

These are lively, robin-like birds, mostly living on hillsides, rocky accumulations and ruins, commonly having noticeable white rumps, which is sometimes the only feature one is aware of as they flit away up the hillsides. Eleven species have been recorded in Iran, and their distribution has been the subject of a study by Cornwallis (1979). The fact that there are so many of this family in Iran is suggested as evidence of the country's geographic and climatic relationship to other surrounding countries. Some of the species are quite hard to distinguish from each other and others occupy similar but slightly different habitats. Their generic Persian name, *Chek chek,* is onomatopoeic for their characteristic alarm call which is uttered whenever a human intruder is in the vicinity of their nests, built in walls or stony caverns or on the ground. They are mostly summer migrants.

WHITE-THROATED ROBIN
(*Irania gutturalis*; Persian: *Sineh-sorkh*)

This lively small bird, also known as the "Persian Robin", is very common in summer in Iran in its favourite habitats, which include oak forest, bushy hillsides and valleys with Cedar covering. It is very variable in appearance, although not all that easily seen, as it tends to skulk in thick cover. Unusually, both sexes sing well, their song somewhat resembling the European Robin's.

THE TITMICE

(Paridae)

Seven members of this family occur in Iran.

BEARDED TIT
(*Panurus biamarcus*; Persian: *Charkh risak-e-neyzar*)

As might be expected, its habitat requirements restrict it to reed-beds, and it is in fact only found in localised areas south of the Caspian.

LONG-TAILED TIT
(*Aegithalos caudatus;* Persian: *Charkh risak-e-dom deraz*)

A resident species in much of the north of the country, inhabiting forests and ground with thick vegetation cover.

SOMBRE TIT
(*Parus lugubris;* Persian: *Charkh risak-e-sar siah*)

Occupies much the same sort of country as the Long-tailed Tit.

The COAL TIT (*Parus ater,* Persian: *Chark risak-e-Pass-e-sar sphid*), the BLUE TIT (*Parus caerulus;* Persian: *Charkh risak-e-sar abi*), and the GREAT TIT (*Parus major,* Persian: *Charkh risak-e-bozorg*) all occupy wooded country in the northern part of the country and are common residents.

PENDULINE TIT (*Remiz pendulinus;* Persian: *Chark risak-e-posht balooti*) has four different races ascribed to it in Iran; they are mainly geographical variations. All are common residents where they occur.

The TURKESTAN TIT (*Parus bokharensis;* Persian: *Charkh risak-e-Tourani*) only occurs rarely in Khorasan Province.

BEE-EATERS

(Meropidae)

Three members of this family of brilliant and colourful birds are found in Iran, of which the L I T T L E   G R E E N   B E E - E A T E R (*Merops orientalis*; Persian: *Zamboo khorak-e-Kouchak*) is the only resident, breeding in the dry habitats of Sistan and to the north of the Persian Gulf. The other two species are summer migrants, familiar to travellers to the country as they sit in colonies on telegraph wires, swooping away every now and then in pursuit of insects. They nest in sandy banks in holes which they excavate themselves.

The B E E - E A T E R (*Merops apiaster*; Persian: *Zanboor Khour-e-Mamooli*) is also well known in southern Europe and is widespread in the summer, except where its place is taken by the Little Green Bee-Eater. The B L U E - C H E E K E D   B E E - E A T E R (*Merops superciliosus*; Persian *Zanier Khour galou Kormaie*) is also known as the Persian Bee-eater in the west and has brilliant iridescent green plumage, which is seen to great advantage as it flies over the dust-brown remains of old palaces and dried out-gardens. It has a rather more northerly distribution than the preceding species.

WAGTAILS AND PIPITS

(Motacillidae)

There are four wagtails to be found in Iran. The C I T R I N E W A G T A I L (*Motacilla citreola*; Persian: *Dom jonbanak-e-kalleh zard*)

165

is a wintering bird only, arriving in large numbers. The YELLOW WAGTAIL (*Motacilla flava*; Persian: *Dom jonbanek-e-zard*) is a summer migrant, breeding in many parts of the country except the very hot southern regions, as does the GREY WAGTAIL (*Motacilla cinerea*; Persian: *Dom jonbarek-e-khakestari*) and the very familiar WHITE WAGTAIL (*Motacilla alba*; Persian: *Dom jonbarek-e-ablagh*) which is found in towns, gardens and farms and stream banks, often in close association with Man.

Tawny Pipit   Photo: Aquila Photographics / Hanne & Jens Eriksen

Of the Pipits (*Anthus spp*), the TAWNY PIPIT (*Anthus campestris*; Persian: *Pepet-e-khaki*) is not uncommon, particularly in mountainous areas. It is quite a large bird for a Pipit; like most of its family it sings on the wing, rising into the air and then planing down to the ground. There are several other Pipits breeding in Iran, including the largest of them, the LONG-BILLED PIPIT, (*Anthus similis*; Persian: *Pepet-e-nok deraz*) which is a high altitude bird breeding in the mountains of the southern provinces. The TREE PIPIT (*Anthus trivialis*; Persian: *Pepet-e-derabkti*) breeds in the north and north-western provinces; while the MEADOW PIPIT (*Anthus pratensis*; Persian: *Pepet-e-sabraie*) is mainly a winter visitor in some numbers in the northern half of the country, as is the RED-THROATED PIPIT (*Anthus cervinus*; Persian: *Pepet-e-Gabo sorkh*) to the south Caspian area and Khusistan.

FINCHES

(Fringillidae)

Finches are represented by 17 species in Iran, most of which will be recognised easily by European visitors to the country. However, there are some which are not generally found in Europe, such as the SNOW FINCH (*Montifringilla nivalis*; Persian: *Gonzesh-e-barfi*) and the WHITE-WINGED GROSBEAK (*Mycerobas carnipes*; Persian: *Sebreb-e-siab*), both of which are high altitude birds; the DESERT FINCH (*Rhodopechys obsoleta*; Persian: *Sebreb-e-khaki*), TRUMPETER FINCH (*Rhodopechys githaginea*; Persian: *Sebreb-e-soorati*), CRIMSON-WINGED FINCH (*Rhodopechys sanguinea*; Persian: *Sebreb-e-boll sorkh*) and the MONGOLIAN TRUMPETER FINCH (*Rhodopechys mongolica*; Persian: *Sebreb-e-mogboli*), which are all rather similar birds with an Asian distribution, bearing stout, bullfinch-like beaks, the cocks tending to red or pink colouration, with females more cryptic. Some of them, like the Desert Finch, have characteristic flight-calls ("a ripling 'r-r-r-e' which descends in pitch and rises" (Moor and Boswell, 1956) and the Trumpeter Finch with a call like "the distant sound of a child's toy trumpet" (Mountfort, 1965) or "a very small puncture under water" (Moor and Boswell, 1956). Another attractive bird, though living at high altitudes, often above the snow-line, is the Golden-fronted Serin (*Serinus pusillus*; Persian: *Sehreh-e-Pishani sorkh*) which is a resident in Iran and descends to lower ground in the winter.

Trumpeter Finch
Photo: Aquila Photographics / Conrad Greaves

168

WARBLERS

(Family: *Sylviidae*)

The Warblers are a huge family of widely distributed insectivorous small birds. Most of them are of a brownish colouration and summer migrants to the northern hemisphere, although some 11 species are residents in Iran, which has 36 Warblers recorded. As passage migrants of course, they are observed in the spring and autumn and some of them breed regularly in suitable habitats. Nearly all of them are highly vocal, some with well developed songs, others with monotonous creaking or buzzing calls. Many are exceedingly shy and cryptic besides, so that often the only indication of their presence is a large noise coming out of a thick bush or reed bed. This family is one of the most testing for ornithologists in the matter of identification and most records will need confirmation by someone familiar with the particular species.

ORIOLES

(Family: *Oriolidae*)

GOLDEN ORIOLE
(*Oriolus oriolus*; Persian: *Pary shahrokh*)

This beautiful bird is familiarly met with in forests and gardens in the north-west of Iran, and is common in the more leafy areas around

Tehran. Surprisingly cryptic, in spite of the male's plumage, it is given away by its mellow calls. A summer migrant, it occurs elsewhere in the country during migration.

STARLINGS

(Family: *Sturnidae*)

COMMON STARLING
(*Sturnus vulgaris*; Persian: *Sara*)

Breeds throughout Iran and is a common resident.

ROSE-COLOURED STARLING
(*Sturnus roseus*; Persian: *Sar-e-sourati*)

Breeds only in the northern and north-western provinces.

COMMON MYNAH
(*Acridotheres tristis*; Persian: *Mina*)

Breeds and is resident in the most southerly and eastern corner of the country. Populous in towns, tame and noisy, they nest in gutters and crevices of buildings.

Common Mynah   Photo: Aquila Photographics / Mike Lane

SPARROWS

(Family: *Ploceidae*)

The H O U S E S P A R R O W (*Passer domesticus;* Persian: *Gonzeshg-e-Mamooli)* and in the east the T R E E S P A R R O W (*Passer montanus;* Persian: *Gonzeshg-e-derakh-ti)* are the commonest and most familiar sparrows in Iran, sometimes forming large and noisy communal roosts in towns. There are a number of other sparrows, mostly restricted to localities by habitat constraints, although some, like the S P A N I S H S P A R R O W (*Passer hispanidensis;* Persian: *Gonzeshg-e-sineh-siah*), are numerous where they occur.

171

10th or 11th Century, possibly depicting a sparrow!

Photo: E. Kahrom

SUNBIRDS

(Family: *Nectarinidae*)

The PURPLE SUNBIRD (*Nectarinia asiatica*; Persian: *Shahd khor*) is the only Iranian representative of this primarily African family. It occurs in large numbers in the most southerly provinces and is often seen in pairs chasing insects or probing for nectar in the flowers of the somewhat dry habitat. A resident species.

172

KINGFISHERS

(Family: *Alcedinidae*)

The commonest Kingfisher is the one familiar in Europe, the
K I N G F I S H E R (*Alcedo athhis*; Persian: *Mahi Khorak-e-Kouchak*). It
is widely distributed, apart from the Persian Gulf, and breeds.

PIED KINGFISHER
(*Ceryle Rudis;* Persian: *Mahi Khorak-e-Ablagh*)

A widespread common species in Khusistan. There are some records of
it in the north-west. It fishes in fresh and sea water alike.

WHITE-BREASTED KINGFISHER
(*Halcyon smyrnensis*; Persian: *Mahi Khorah-e-Sineh sephid*)

A resident of southern Iran,
breeding in fairly large
numbers, commonly seen
perching on telephone
wires, often at some
distance from water.

White-breasted Kingfisher
Photo: R. Ghaemi

173

HERONS, BITTERNS AND EGRETS

(Family: *Ardeidae*)

Most of the birds in this family are fish and/or insect eaters with long legs and beaks, and as such are found in and around marshes, reed-beds and bodies of water.

BITTERN

(*Botaurus stellaris*; Persian: *Bootimar*)

Well known in the Caspian region and the marshes of Sistan and Khusistan, where it is thought to breed occasionally. However, most Bitterns in Iran are wintering birds.

LITTLE BITTERN

(*Ixobrychus minutus*; Persian: *Boutimar-e-kouchak*)

Breeds in Iran in large numbers as a summer migrant.

NIGHT HERON

(*Nyctocorax nyctocorax*; Persian: *Havasil-e-shah*)

Breeds in the Caspian region and the western provinces, with a few breeding in Sistan. Those in Khusistan appear to be resident, but the rest of the Iranian population is migratory.

LITTLE GREEN HERON
(*Boturides striatus*; Persian: *Havasil-e-sabz*)

A solitary, but not uncommon species resident in the marshes of the Persian Gulf.

SQUACCO HERON
(*Ardeola ralloides*; Persian: *Havasil-e-zard*)

A summer breeder in the north, west and Khusistan areas, a few wintering in the south-west.

INDIAN POND HERON
(*Ardeola grayii*; Persian: *Havasil-e-hendi*)

A rare resident of the marshes of the Persian Gulf.

CATTLE EGRET
(*Bubulcus ibis*; Persian: *Gav cheranek*)

Breeds in large numbers in the Caspian region and is also found on the Khusistan marshes. It is frequently found in the company of cattle and buffaloes as its name implies.

GREAT WHITE HERON
(*Egretta alba*; Persian: *Egret-e-bozorg*)

A mainly wintering species on marshland anywhere in the country.

LITTLE EGRET
(*Egretta garzetta*; Persian: *Egret-e-kouchale*)

A plentiful species, breeding in the Caspian region and Lake Reziaieh wetlands. Winters in the Khusistan marshes.

WESTERN REEF HERON
(*Egretta gularis*; Persian: *Egret-e-saheli*)

Confined to the northern coasts of the Persian Gulf, where it is resident in the salt-marshes of the region.

GREY HERON
(*Ardea cinerea*; Persian: *Havasil-e-Khakestari*)

A very common bird, breeding in the north and west; wintering throughout the country.

PURPLE HERON
(*Ardea purpurea*; Persian: *Havasil-e-Arghavani*)

This handsome heron has much the same breeding grounds as the Grey Heron, but few spend the winter in the country.

GOLIATH HERON
(*Ardea goliath*; Persian; *Havasil e-bozorg*)

A rarity in Iran; when it is seen it is usually in the vast marshes and wetlands of Baluchistan.

PIGEONS AND DOVES

(Family: *Columbidae*)

The association of pigeons with mosques, shrines and similar holy places has given them a "respectable" status among Iranians and they are fed and cared for by the worshippers.

The C O L L A R E D   D O V E (*Streptopelia decaocto*; Persian: *Ya karim*) is in fact thought to be calling the name of God in its monotonous song, hence its name in Persian, meaning "O God!"

The W O O D   P I G E O N (Columba palumbus; Persian: *Kabootar-e-zangali*) and the S T O C K   D O V E (*Columa oenas*; Persian: *Fakteh*) breed plentifully in the north and west and are common resident

species. The E A S T E R N S T O C K   D O V E (*Columba eversmanni*; Persian: *Fahk-e-Khavari*) has a small population in the north of Khorassan. The T U R T L E   D O V E (*Streptopelia turtur*; Persian: *Ghomri-e-mammoli*) is a widely distributed summer visitor, breeding everywhere except in the far south.

Turtle dove
Photo: late H. R. Biat

177

SANDGROUSE

(Family: *Pteroclididae*)

As befits a country with such a great area of dry and desert land, Iran is the home of no less than seven species of these interesting birds. Closely related to pigeons, they have many of the same behavioural characteristics. They need water and drink like pigeons, in spite of living in a desert environment; therefore they will never nest farther from water than they can conveniently fly at least once a day. There are stories of desert explorers being saved from death by thirst after noting the direction of the evening flights of flocks of sandgrouse as they flew to a water-hole to drink. The nest is a mere scrape in the sand, and, again like pigeons, they lay two eggs and operate a shift system between the pair. The males are often handsomely coloured, but the females are invariably cryptic, merging to invisibility against the desert background. Extremely social birds, they form huge flocks, and

Female Sandgrouse with chicks drinking.   Photo: E. Kahrom

have always been a favourite prey species for shooters and falconers. The most plentiful species are the P I N T A I L E D   S A N D G R O U S E (*Pterocles alchata;* Persian: *Koukar-e-shekam sephid*), and the B L A C K - B E L L I E D   S A N D G R O U S E (*Pterocles Orientals;* Persian: *Koukar-e-skekam siab*). All are resident, except P A L L A S ' S S A N D G R O U S E (*Syrrhaptes pradoxus*), a rare winter visitor to the north.

Lichtenstein's Sandgrouse   Photo: late H. R. Biat

Black-bellied Sandgrouse   Photo: late H. R. Biat

SHRIKES

(Family: *Laniidae*)

The Shrikes are mostly resident, or partly resident, birds which breed in most of the country; some, such as the M A S K E D   S H R I K E (*Lanius nubicus*; Persian: *Sang Cheshim-e-Pishani Sephid*), being particularly associated with olive orchards; while the I S A B E L L I N E   S H R I K E (*Lanius Isabellinus*; Persian: *Sang Chesm-e-dom sorkh*), as its name implies, is a resident of dry scrubby land. The commonest shrike is the R E D - B A C K E D   S H R I K E (*Lanius collurio*; Persian: *Sang Chesm-e-Posht sorkh*). Shrikes become particularly observable in the autumn, when many are moving through the country, and can be seen perching on wires or prominent posts on the look-out for prey. Ticehurst et al

(1930) found the G R E A T   G R E Y   S H R I K E (*Lanius excubitor*; Persian: *Sang-Chesm Bozorg*) very common and breeding in large numbers on some tiny islands they surveyed in the Persian Gulf.

Red-backed Shrike
Photo: Aquila Photographics / Kevin Carlson

WRENS

(Family: *Troglodytidae*)

WREN

(*Troglodytes troglodydes*; Persian: *Elikaie*)

A common and much loved resident of the northern regions of Iran and in the Zagros mountain area.

Wren　　　　Photo: Aquila Photographics / Mike Lane

DIPPER

(Family: *Cinclidae*)

DIPPER

(*Cinclus cinclus*; Persian: *Zir-ab-roak*)

A rather rare bird in Iran, but has been found ocasionally along mountain streams in the west.

Dipper.
Photo: Aquila Photographics / Mike Lane

GULLS AND TERNS

(Family: *Laridae*)

The Caspian Sea in the north, the Persian Gulf in the south, and numerous lakes and marshes in between, make Iran an attractive country for gulls and terns, and the mild climate in some of the marshlands makes them suitable wintering grounds. The commonest breeding gull is the S L E N D E R - B I L L E D G U L L (*Larus genei*; Persian: *Kakaie-ye-posht shah*), which nests in large numbers on lakes and islands, and winters in the country as well. The H E R R I N G G U L L (*Larus argentatus*; Persian: *Kakaie-ye-nogh-rehie*) is a common wintering bird and breeds colonially on the islands of Lake Rezaieh. Most of the remaining seven or so species are met in the winter only, with the exception of the B L A C K - H E A D E D G U L L (*Larus ridibundus*; Persian: *Kakiae-ye-sar-siah*) which has a smallish breeding group nesting at Lake Reziaeh.

T E R N S

(*Sternidac*; Persian: *Parastooye-Dariaie*)

The Persian name translates as "Swallow of the water". A number of them breed, in and around the Caspian area; such as the Caspian (*Hydrprogne tschegrava*), G U L L - B I L L E D T E R N (*Gelochelidon nilotica*), W H I S K E R E D T E R N (*Chelidonias hybrida*), while the G R E A T - C R E S T E D T E R N (*Sterna bergii*), Lesser-Crested Tern (*Sterna bengalensis*), W H I T E - C H E E K E D T E R N (*Sterna repressa*) B R I D L E D T E R N (*Sterna anaethetus*), and S A U N D E R ' S L I T T L E T E R N (*Sterna saundersi*) are mainly Persian Gulf birds.

Crested Tern   Photo: Aquila Photographics / Conrad Greaves

The LITTLE TERN (*Sterna albifrons*) is widely distributed in Iran, breeding on the sandy shores of lakes and sea-coasts and the marshlands.

CORMORANTS

(Family: *Phalacrocoracidae*)

CORMORANT
(*Phalacrocorax carbo*; Persian: *Baklan*)

This is common on both northern and southern coasts, breeding in colonies in the marshes of the Caspian area and wintering in large numbers in the Persian Gulf.

184

SOCOTRA CORMORANT
(*Phalacrocorax nigrogularis*; Persian: *Baklan-e-galoo siah*)

Lives exclusively on the islands of the Persian Gulf, where it is a resident and breeds in large numbers.

PIGMY CORMORANT
(*Phalacrocorax pygmaeus*; Persian: *Baklan-e-Kouchak*)

Plentiful in Iran in the winter. There is a small breeding population in the northern marshes.

Pigmy Cormorant   Photo: Aquila Photographics / J. L. Roberts

CUCKOOS

(Family: *Cuculidae*)

CUCKOO
(*Cuculus canorus*; Persian: *Kuckoo*)

A summer migrant, it breeds over most of Iran, except the far south-east.

GREAT SPOTTED CUCKOO
(*Clamator glandarius*; Persian: *Kookoo ye-kahl dar*)

A summer visitor, breeding only among the high grounds of the north and west. It parasitizes crows and sometimes jays, laying several eggs in a nest.

Great spotted Cuckoo
Photo: Aquila Photographics /
Mike Wilkes

PIED CRESTED CUCKOO
(*Clamator jacobinus*; Persian: *Kookoo taj dar*)

A much smaller bird than the preceding ones, its breeding range is limmited to the Azerbayjan region, although it is seen further south on migration.

NIGHTJARS

(Family: *Caprimulgudae*)

NIGHTJAR
(*Caprimulgus europeus;* Persian: *Shabgard*)

A summer visitor, breeding in the forests and woodlands of the north-west.

EGYPTIAN NIGHTJAR
(*Caprimulgus aegypticus;* Persian: *Shabgard-e-dashti*)

A rather large, pale nightjar breeding in the eastern desert country, and sometimes met out of season in Baluchistan.

The two other nightjars, the INDIAN NIGHTJAR (*Caprimulgus asiaticus*) and SYKES' NIGHTJAR (*Caprimulgus mahrattensis*) have a wider distribution and are found in much of the mountainous north and west of the country.

Nightjar   Photo: Aquila Photographics / John Lawton

NUTHATCHES AND CREEPERS

(Family: *Sittidae*)

This small family of birds is well represented in Iran, but only two of them are likely to be noticed by visitors. These are Neumayer's Rock Nuthatch (*Sitta neumayer*, Persian *Kamarkoli-e-bozorg*) and the Wall Creeper (*Tichodroma muraria*, Persian: *Divar khazak*). The first species will be heard rather than seen, as it is a very noisy bird,

188

frequenting rock faces and commonly encountered in the neighbourhood of the inscriptions and rock carvings which seem to have been the favourite method of advertising in times gone by. It has a variety of loud calls, but more persistently a loud trilling noise which is difficult to locate, and which echoes among the rocks – all part of the sometimes lonely and romantic atmosphere of these locations. The spectacular Wall Creeper is much rarer and seems to like really remote mountainous crags as a habitat. Its manner of flicking its butterfly shaped wings as it jerks itself up a vertical cliff-face, showing off scarlet flashes as it does so, makes it another bird which, once seen, will never be forgotten.

WOODPECKERS

(Family: *Picidae*)

For a country that has so much dry land and desert, Iran has a surprising number of woodpeckers. This may be due to its geographical position, so that as in the case of Wheatears, Woodpecker species from all the surrounding countries have come in and settled in any suitable habitat available. The so-called "Pied" woodpeckers, all closely related, comprise six recorded species. There are two "greens": the GREEN WOODPECKER (*Picus viridis*; Persian: *Darkoob-be-zabz*) and the SCALY-BELLIED WOODPECKER (*Picus Squamatus*). The great BLACK WOODPECKER (*Dryocopus martius*; Persian: *Darkoob siah*) can be found in suitable habitat over most of the northern half of the country.

Green Woodpecker, adult and juvenile.   Photo: Aquila Photographics / A. T. Moffett

WADING BIRDS

(Families: *Charadiidae, Haematopodidae*)

This large group of birds, known to Eurpeans as Waders and to Americans as Shore-birds, is well represented in Iran. The great marshes of the Caspian region and the lonely plains and isolated pools which form after the winter rains, offer suitable, if temporary, habitat for many of them. Besides which, Iran lies on the direct migration routes for many of the High Arctic breeders, and during passage birds in various stages of bright nuptial plumage can be found exploiting quite tiny ponds and trickles of water almost anywhere, even in dry and desert locations. But the Caspian region probably holds the greatest concentration of waders at all seasons, particularly during the equinoxes when huge numbers of birds may be present, both resident and migratory, their ariel manoeuvres in vast flocks forming a constantly changing kaleidoscope of pattern and colour which is unlikely ever to be forgotten. The flocks of ducks, geese and cranes with all the waders gathered in great masses make the area one of the great ornithological sites of the world.

There are also sizeable populations of waders moving up and down the Persian Gulf, many using this more southerly and westerly migration route between Africa and the Arctic.

Black winged Stilt, at Karkhe.   Photo: E. Kahrom

One of the more interesting species of this group is the C R A B P L O V E R (*Dromus ardeola*; Persian: *Salime kharchang khor*). Breeding in sometimes large colonies along the Persian Gulf, it excavates burrows in which it lays its eggs. Its food consists of crabs and other surface dwelling creatures which frequent the tidal mud. According to Scott (1988) it has a preference for the very glutinous mud found in and around mangrove swamps, but this may just reflect the habitat of its prey. There is some dispersion out of the Gulf after the breeding season.

LARKS

(Family: *Alaudidae*)

Iran is well blessed with larks and 17 species occupy almost every sort of habitat; their songs are always a pleasurable feature of the countryside. To the casual traveller they are very confusing, mostly appearing as brownish birds flying up from the way-side as one's car or bus passes by. Away from the roads, a variety of melodious calls and short songs fill the air, the birds themselves being invisible among the vegetation. The S K Y - L A R K (*Alauda arvensis*; Persian: *Chakavak-e-Assemani*) sings in flight with a sustained song as well. Larks are sociable birds and like to live within sound of each other, even when breeding. They often form large flocks at other times. They are not all that difficult to identify once seen in the binoculars and it is then possible to relate a particular bird to a song or call in the neighbourhood.

Sky-lark   Photo: Aquila Photographics / Conrad Greaves

PEACOCK

(Pavo cristatus; Persian: *Tavoos)*

This review of Iranian birds began with the Nightingale, a nondescript looking bird with a heart-warming song. To finish, a spectacularly plumaged bird with an appalling voice has also been part of the culture and folk-lore of the Persians for centuries. Strictly speaking, it is not an Iranian bird at all, but is a native of the Indian jungles and forested slopes of the Himalayas, where its loud shrieks carry from valley to valley in a much more romantic way than in an urban environment. It has been a partially domesticated bird for a long time and there are a number of colour variations, such as white. There are too, some distinct wild species of Peafowl, some of which are now rare due to forest destruction in their home ranges.

The famous "Peacock Throne", so-called because of the multiplicity of its embedded jewels, was brought to Iran from the Mogul Empire by Nadir Shah, but peacocks themselves were well known in the country long before his time.

Ella Sykes (1910) recounted that peacocks were only allowed to be kept by royalty (although an exception was made for the British Ambassador). However, it appears that they were also of particular significance to those of the Zoroastrian religion and it is interesting that a couple of fine peacocks are illustrated in the tilework of the inner-courtyard entrance arch of the great Friday Mosque at Kerman. This town was one of the main centres of Zoroastrianism in the 19th Century, and for a long time before, so that there may have been some influence of a local nature brought to bear when the mosque was decorated.

The Yezidi sect, established in northern Kurdistan, which has obscure origins including Zoroastrian and Manichaen ones, also holds the peacock in respect (Guest 1993).

In popular imagination not all of the peacock is beautiful. According to Sa'adi, "People admire the Peacock for his colourful plumage, but the poor bird himself is ashamed of his ugly legs."

A HISTORY OF POLO IN IRAN

Nobody knows when exactly Man managed to tame horses and put saddles on their backs. Polo, or *Chougan* as the Persians call it, seems to have started soon after riding began, so it is a truly ancient sport.

An ancestral version of the game is recorded in Chinese and Persian manuscripts as early as 600 B.C. as a pastime of royal courts in Asia and Asia-Minor. The word "Polo" is of Tibetan origin: *Pu-Lu*, meaning willow root, which is what the ball is made of. It was then a sport mingled with pageantry, involving numerous players (women also had their teams) and hundreds of ponies. But the principle was the same: two mounted teams dispute the possession of a ball and attempt to strike it with flexible mallets through enemy goal-posts at each end of a long, grassy playing field.

Polo has been a popular sport in Iran since 860 B.C. Kings, princes, aristrocrats and military men, showed great interest in it and this has been documented in the works of the poets and authors of the time. As one of the oldest of sports, polo and its laws and regulations has been mentioned in history books, dictionaries, stories and paintings from the time of the Sassanians to the end of the Safavid and Zandieh era.

So popular was the pastime, and people took so much pleasure in it, that almost all the poets from Roodaki to those living during Zandieh reflected it in their work. However, for our purposes, only one or two from each century will be quoted. One of the greatest epics of all, Firdowsi's *Shahnama*, which has been extant for the last eleven centuries, repeatedly mentions the tradition of *chougan* from prehistoric times to the Sassanians.

The first story in which Firdowsi mentions the sport concerns Siavash Kiani. Siavesh and Garseevas, two of the most famous Pahlavans of *The Shahnama*, play *chougan* from early morning onwards. Garseevas starts the game by throwing the ball into the field and Siavash hits it so hard that the sky accepts it as a gift and never returns it!

The second story concerns the pastime of *Haft-gordan* (seven generals). When Roslen wanted to entertain his friends (all famous generals) he invited them to a place called Navand, with the most beautiful palaces and *chougan* fields. In this place the Pahlavans either hunted or played polo. "This is the proper way to entertain your noble friends and royalty."

After the Kiaman dynasty there is little mention of *chougan* for about 18 centuries until the Sassanian period. The *Shahnama* relates that Ardeshir and his son Shapour I were particularly keen on the sport. One story has it that Shapour I, unknown to his father, fell in love with a girl called Mehrak. The fruit of this secret affair was a boy named Hormoz. One day when Ardeshir and Shapour went on a hunting trip they came across Hormoz playing polo with his friends. Hormoz was so good that Ardeshir was impressed and asked about his family and descent, because, said he, "only a King's son could play *chougan* so perfectly. "Hormoz mentioned his father's name and thus the secret was revealed.

According to the *Shahnama*, playing *chougan* was a sign of nobility and wisdom. The capability of young men from noble families was measured by their skill at playing polo. Shapour II became a competent player at the age of 17; Bahram-e-Gur was only 18 when he no longer needed anybody to teach him to read and write, train hunting cheetahs, practise falconry, or play *chougan*.

Khosraw Parviz divided each month into four parts; three for ruling the country and the fourth for playing polo and practising archery.

> Then he divided the month into four parts
> to allow him to enjoy his life better.
> He employed a trainer to teach him
> The enjoyments of archery and polo.

THE 9TH CENTURY A.D.

Written during the 9th century, a book of Arabian origin entitled *Al Harb* (The War) relates the methodology of polo. The regulations given in this book are quoted in a Persian book called *Aeen Nameh Pahlavi* (Pahlavi Regulations), although this precious work is no longer with us, and is presumed to have perished. Some of the rules from *Aeen Nameh Pahlavi* are as follows:

1. *Chougan* requires a lot of effort.

2. The polo mallet should be used in such a way that it does not make any marks on the ground.

3. Breaking the mallet is sign of lack of skill.

4. Never use a whip.

5. Never gallop your horse towards another player.

6. Let the horse gallop at its own pace.

7. Never allow yourself to fall off the horse.

8.   Never swear or use bad language, control your rage and be patient.

It seems as if modern sportsmen could learn something from these regulations, too!

10TH CENTURY A.D.

Written after The *Shahnama* by Shah Quaboos to his son, *Quaboosnameh* consists of 44 chapters, the 19th being about *chougan* and its rules and regulations. The king warns his son against becoming addicted to the game.

   In *Tarikh Beihaghi* (History of Beihaghi), one of the kings of the Quaznavi dynasty, to celebrate the construction of his new castle, orders the best players of the day to inaugurate a *chougan* field at his court.

11TH CENTURY A.D.

Omar Khayam uses the game to express some of the most difficult of philosophical and religious concepts, i.e. destiny and fate, acceptance and resignation.

> The Ball no question makes of Ayes and Noes,
> But Right or Left as strikes the Player goes;
> And He that toss'd Thee down into the Field,
> HE knows about it all – He knows – HE knows!
>
> *Rubaiyat of Omar Khayyam (trs. Fitzgerald)*

It is interesting to note that the 19th day of each month in the Iranian Calendar, reorganised in the time of Omar Khayam, was *Gooy- baz* (*Gooy* = ball, *baz* = play), another name for *chougan*. Presumably, the 19th of each month was allotted to playing polo matches.

12TH CENTURY A.D.

Nezami Ganjavi, in the epic of Kusraw and Shirin, tells the following story. One of the Sassanian kings had a daughter called Shirin. She was very beautiful, an excellent rider and a competent polo player. During a trip to the capital her mother counselled her, and some of the other young ladies of the court, about the perils of romance at a young age and love outside marriage. These girls were all skillful polo players and one day when Princess Shirin and her friends were watching a game of polo, Kusraw, who was playing himself, challenged them to a game. They accepted, and when the game started everybody was surprised to see how well they played. Sometimes the King and sometimes the ladies were in the lead and at the end the riders paraded past the spectators. The polo field seems to have been a favourite meeting place for noble couples as well as a place to impress and gain notice!

Iran is the home country of mixed polo and pictures of ladies playing polo have been painted by artists for centuries.

13TH CENTURY A.D.

Saadi, one of the greatest poets of Iran, also mentioned polo in his books and found striking similarities between the polo ball and the breasts of young ladies wrapped in their long black hair! In one description the ball is made of ivory!

14TH CENTURY A.D.

In the poems of Shabastari, the great Soufi of the period, the elements involved in the game of *chougan*, i.e. rider, horse, mallet, ball and field, have been used as symbols of respectively: man, knowledge, determination, goals and the world.

Hafiz also mentions the metaphorical aspects of *chougan* in his masterpiece.

The great Soufi poet of the age, Jami, offers his head as the *chougan* ball for the pleasure of the one he loves:

> That would be the proudest day of my life
> To lose my head for your chougan
> When your lovers throw their heads into your polo field
> I wish all my body were reduced to the size of my head.

(trs. Kahrom)

15TH – 17TH CENTURIES A.D.

During this time polo was extremely popular with the Persians. In Isphafan and Shiraz *chougan* fields were numerous and some of them still exist. In those days the limits of the field were marked by stone posts, and the goal-posts were stone pillars. These markers can still be seen around some of the fields. The famous *chougan* field in Isphahan, the Maidan, is situated in front of the Ali Kapu Palace. It is now a public open space.

THE PRESENT DAY

The future of *chougan* seems to be quite safe in Iran, not only because Iranians love to keep the tradition alive, but also, fortunately, Islam greatly advocates riding – in fact riding and archery are the only sports on which betting is allowed. Polo is now well organised in Iran and attracts as many spectators as ever.

PIGEON TOWERS

Tall, rounded towers, found in the environs of Isphahan and other places, sometimes highly decorated in crude leafy designs, and sometimes crumbling to dust due to lack of repair, have attracted the attention of archeologists visiting the country. They are known as Pigeon Towers, the Iranian equivalent of the French *pigeoniers* which are found in many parts of France, and also in Great Britain, though few survive there. The Iranian towers are on a grand scale, providing accomadation for thousands of birds. Nearly all the European texts suggest that the reason for these towers was to provide the highly nitrogenous manure for the famous melon gardens of the neighbourhood (Stevens, 1961; Beazley, 1966; 1977). However, it is certain that there was another need which these towers satisfied and that was production of pigeons' eggs, which were highly esteemed as delicacies, especially for children. Traditionally, a child who was slow in learning to talk would be given pigeons' eggs to eat. Pigeon meat, although eaten, was not a popular food among the people, the eggs being much more prized.

Not all the towers were of the turret variety. Beazley (1977) saw some in north-west Iran which were rectangular, and "reminiscent of small forts". According to Stevens (1961) many of these towers were built in the time of Shah Abbas, but it seems likely that in fact these were replacements of earlier ones, as pigeon keeping has been a minor domestic enterprise for many thousands of years. As one of Persia's ingenious alternative technologies, which have been evolved as survival strategies by the inhabitants of a harsh environment, pigeon towers are almost the precursors of modern intensive agriculture; the advantage was that the upkeep of pigeons was presumably fairly cheap, as they could range widely and freely subsisting on wild seeds or other peoples' grain. The construction of high towers with a secured base would have protected the birds from snakes, and possibly the only predators they had to fear were intinerant falcons and owls.

Some of these towers are still in use, and supply a traditonal need, although melons nowadays are more likely to be grown using artificial fertiliser. Modern Iranians are more interested in Racing Pigeons than the culinary variety.

A HISTORY OF FALCONRY
IN IRAN

There are many theories concerning the earliest records of falconry being practised by Man; however, Amiett (1977) records an engraving on a stele found near Marsh (present-day Turkey) which shows a young child standing on his mother's lap, holding in his hand a leash which secures a hawk of some sort by jesses attached to its legs. The archeological dating for this stele is approximately 2000 B.C. We cannot tell from this if the stele is in fact evidence of serious falconry being practiced in the region, or if it is just a quaint portrayal of a little boy with a pet bird. However, it seems unlikely that the stele was carved out for fun; it could be thought that some monarch, already addicted to the chase, commissioned the stele in the hope that the art of falconry would become part of the curriculum princelings would follow as they grew up and left the nursery. We could even speculate that the child represents a king, and the woman in whose lap he is standing, is in fact a goddess, an early forerunner of Diana, who is showing her protective aspects for hunters and hawkers. Historical speculation of this sort needs corroboration by other instances; if however, given the general hunting and chasing culture of the times, there seems no reason to suppose that other evidence will not be unearthed in the future.

It is still not clear when the art of training falcons to hunt under controlled conditions for the amusement and benefit of Man became generally known. Given the behavioural propensity of birds to remain attached to their earliest rearers (i.e. "imprinting"), it was probably bound to happen sooner or later; but it is interesting that primitive hunter-gatherer societies which have existed in Africa, America and Australia do not seem to have developed the art at all, though using other animals, such as dogs, to assist them in pursuit of terrestrial prey.

What little evidence we have suggests that falconry was evolved in Asia, possibly China. It was mentioned by Marco Polo as being practised there during the 13th Century, but by that time it was practised by European nobility and was already somewhat regulated, so that only certain ranks could fly certain species of hawk. In Iran, all we have is the belief of Firdowsi that falconry began in prehistoric times, although this is vague to say the least.

The earliest written evidence seems to lie in a book entitled *Javareh Nameh*, in which it is stated that Anoushirvan was the first Iranian king to order information on the subject to be collected. Later, a chapter about the Peregrine Falcon was added and the book was used by falconers for many years. During the Seljuk era, Malek Shah ordered it to be updated and perfected, a process which took thirty years to complete. Copies of this book are still extant and can be used by contemporary falconers.

In Sassanian times falconry was much in vogue, and like European noble society of the period, a well-trained falcon was a valuable gift to be presented to royalty or other influential folk.

Most of the Safavid kings were keen on the sport, none more so than the great Shah Abbas, who had a very large aviary to house his hawks. Once, when one was killed out hunting, the king ordered a monument to be built in its memory. This can still be seen on a hill near Yazd.

After the Safavids the art of falconry was neglected, with only a few people keeping it going. The Quajar monarchs revived it somewhat. M. Abel Boyer, the French falconer who visited Iran in 1910, wrote that "you could see the people around with their falcons sitting on their wrists". The birds were often carried to noisy and crowded parts of towns, such as bazaars, to tame them.

During this period a comprehensive book appeared entitled *Baznameh-e Naseri* (Naser's Book of Falcons) which is still used by falconers and has been translated into several European languages. Today, falconry remains popular and information about the sport is exchanged on a world-wide basis.

The Department of the Environment, which is responsible for wildlife protection in Iran, has been prominent in publication of articles and the promotion of bird of prey conservation to falconers (the late General A. Nasrollahi, pers. comm.). All species of raptor are protected in Iran and a number of ringing studies have been carried out to determine patterns of distribution and behaviour of Merlins and Peregrine Falcons. In this, falconers have played a leading role and are mostly staunch allies of the conservation movement.

In general, falconry has been, and remains, the activity of a few dedicated people who have the time, resources and temperaments to engage in this ancient but demanding sport.

There are large numbers of paintings, tiles and similar artefacts which show falconers with hawks on their wrists; or free-flying hawks; unfortunately it is not always possible to determine the species of hawk being used, except that museum curators have occasionally made wild guesses and labelled a merlin as an eagle for instance, probably due to ignorance of the sport and ornithology Scarce, J. (1989), writing about two very fine Saker Falcons on tile-work in the Hasht Bihisht Palace at Isphahan, decribes them as parrots!

Ref. *Shekar va Tabiat* is the monthly magazine of the Department of the Environment in Tehran, and contains numbers of articles and features on falconry, including some by General Nasrollahi, who was a prominent authority on the subject in his lifetime.

CHRONOLOGY

B.C.

2500	Pyramids built.
2000	Sumerians at Ur. Horses, Onagers, Cattle, Sheep, Felted Clothes.
1736	Hammurabi at Babylon, Code of Legal Practice.
1405	Amenhotep III at Luxor, Egypt. Egyptians worshipped cats, ibises, hawks, and mummified them.
1351	Akenaton (husband of Nefertiti) Egypt 1361 Tutankamen Egypt
1322	Moses Exodus Egypt
1286	Ramases II. Abu Simnel statues Egypt. 1246 Joshua, Israelites enter Canaan "Flowing with milk and honey"
1146	Nebucadnessar I Babylon
1022	David; Israel. 968 Solomon Israel. Temple at Jerusalem built with wood from Syria
834	Assyryians invade Medes and Persians
842	Ahab; Jezebel and Jehu, Chariot Wars. Israel
879	Shalmaneser III Assyria. Siege of Jerusalem Death of Assyrian Army – Plague?
550-530	Cyrus the Great, sets up Persian Empire
490	Battle of Marathon
522-486	Darius I

486   Darius I, Persia Persepolis constructed

486   Battles of Thermopylae and Salamis

466   Xerxes I Persia

465-24   Artaxerxes

456   Pericles Greece

334-323   Alexander the Great
           Burns Persepolis
           Dies in Babylon

A.D.

210   Shapur I (Capture of Valerian)

147-90   Destruction of Ctesiphon by Marcus Aurelius. Sassanians

312-224   Seleucids and Parthians

420-38   Bahram Gur

c. 520   Birth of Mohammed

651   Arab Conquest of Persia

786-809   Harun-el-Rashid rules in Baghdad

c. 970   Firdawsi – Author of Shahnama

1219   Genghis Khan and Mongols invade West

1256   Hulagu – Destruction of Baghdad

1271   Marco Polo passes through Persia

c. 1336   Rumi, Saadi and Hafiz, Poets

1380	Tamberlane conquers Persia
1447	Ulugh Beg (Astronomer at Samarkand)
1587	Shah Abbas the Great
1797-1834	Fath Ali Shah
1925	Reza Khan declared Shah (Persia from now on called Iran)
1941	Mohammed Reza Shah
1979	Shah deposed Ayatollah Khomeini proclaims Islamic Republic followed by 8 years war with Iraq

Amiet, P., 1977, *L'Art Antique du Prochaine Orient,* Editions D'Art Lucien Mazenod, Paris

Arnold, A., 1877, *Through Persia by Caravan,* Tinsley Bros., London

Beazley, E., 1966, The Pigeon Towers of Isfahan, in *Iran IV,* p.105

Beazley, E., 1977, some Vernacular Buildings of the Iranian Plateau, in *Iran XV,* p.101

Bokonyi, S., 1976, Development of Early Stock Raising in the Near East, in *Nature,* 264:19-23

Burton, R. F., 1855, *A Personal Narrative of a Pilgrimage to Al-Madinah and Meccah,* ed. Lady Burton, Bohn G. Bell and Sons, London (reprinted 1915)

Buxton, P. A., 1921, Notes on Birds from Western and Northern Persia, in *Journal of the Bombay National History Society,* Vol.27, pp.844-882

Chapman, M. J., 1991, Camels, in *Biologist,* 38:2, pp.41-44

Champion-Jones, N. I., 1945, Occurrence of the Lion in Persia, in *Journal of the Bombay National History Society,* Vol.44

Cornwallis, L., 1975, *The Comparative Ecology of Eleven Species of Wheatear (Genus Oenanthe) in S. W. Iran,* D. Phil. Thesis (Oxford)

Cramp, S., ed., 1977, *Handbook of the Birds of Europe, the Middle East, and North Africa (the Birds of the Western Palaearctic),* Oxford University Press (specifically excludes Iran in geographical surveys)

Crawshay-Williams, E., 1907, *Across Persia,* Edward Arnold, London

De Misonne, X., 1968, Mammals, in *Cambridge History of Iran,* Vol.1, ed. A. J. Arberry, Cambridge University Press, pp. 1, 9, 294-304

Doughty, C. M., 1908, *Wanderings in Arabia,* abr. Garnett, Duckworth, London

Ebrahim Poor, M. T., 1974, *Chougan (Polo) in Iran,* Bank Meli Press, Tehran, Iran

Heaney, G. F., 1943, Occurrence of the Lion in Persia, in *Journal of the Bombay National History Society,* Vol.44, p.467

Herodotus: The Histories, trs. Aubrey de Selincourt, 1954, Penguin Classics

Housego, J., 1989, Carpets, in *The Arts of Persia,* ed. R. W. Ferrier, pp.118-157, Yale University Press

Hué, F. and Etchcopar, R. D., 1970, *Les Oiseaux du Proche et du Moyen Orient,* Boubée, Paris

Humphreys, Eileen, 1991, *The Royal Road – A Popular History of Iran,* Scorpion Publishing Ltd., Buckhurst Hill, Essex

Humphreys, P. N., 1977, Ornithological Notes, in *Asian Affairs,* Vol. 64, (Old Series Vol. VIII), Part 1

I.U.C.N. Red Data Book, 1982, Amphibia-Reptilia Part 1, Testudines, Crocodylia, Rhynchocephalia, compiled by B. Groombridge, I.U.C.N., Gland, Switzerland

I.U.C.N. Red Data Book, 1972, Vol.3, Amphibia and Reptilia, compiled by E. Honegger, I.U.C.N. Morges, Switzerland

Edington, J. M., and Edington, M. A., 1986, *Ecology, Recreation and Tourism,* Cambridge University Press, Cambridge, New York and Melbourne

Epstein, H., 1984, Ass, Mule and Onager, in *Evolution of Domesticated Animals,* ed. I. L. Mason, Longman, New York, pp.174-184

Epstein, H., and Mason, I. L., 1984, Cattle, in *Evolution of Domesticated Animals,* ed. I. L. Mason, Longman, New York

Ettinghausen, R., 1979, Bahram Gur's Hunting Feats or the Problem of Identification, *Iran,* Vol. XVII, pp.25-32

Firdawsi, A., 1989, *Shahnama,* Elm Publishers, Tehran

Giri, Felix, 1983, *Animals of Asia,* Hamlyn Publishing Group, London

Guest, J. S., 1993, *Survival Among the Kurds: A History of the Yezidis,* Kegan Paul International, Reviewed Asian Affairs, Vol. XXV, 1994, by Balim-Harsding

Harrington, F. A., and Darrehshooie, B. F., 1975, *A Guide to the Mammals of Iran,* Department of the Environment, Tehran

Jervis, Read, S., 1968, Ornithology, in *Cambridge History of Iran,* Vol. 1, ed. A. J. Arberry, Cambridge University Press, pp. 1, 11, 372-392

King, P., 1986, *Curzon's Persia,* Sidgwick and Jackson, London

Lambton, A. K. S., 1988, *Continuity and Change in Medieval Persia,* I. B. Tauris and Co. Ltd, London

Latifi, Mahmoud, 1991, trs. Sepideh Sajadian, *The Snakes of Iran,* Society for the Study of Amphibians and Reptiles

Lydekker, R., 1912, *The Horse and its Relatives,* George Allen and Company, London

Madjnoonian, H., 1685, National Parks and Natural Reserves, in *Environmental Studies No. 12*, Tehran University Press

Mason, I. L., 1984, Camels, in *Evolution of Domesticated Animals*, ed. I. L. Mason, Longman, New York, pp.106-115

Maxwell, G., 1957, *A Reed Shaken by the Wind*, Longman, London

McLachan, K., 1988, *The Neglected Garden*, I. B. Tauris and Co. Ltd, London

Moor & Boswell, 1956, Field Observations on Birds of Iraq, in *Birds of the Lebanon and Jordan Area*, by S. Vere Benson, 1970, I.C.B.P.

Morgan, D. O., 1986, *The Mongols*, Basil Blackwell, Oxford

Mountfort, G., 1956, *Portrait of a Desert*, Collins, London

Olmstead, A. T., 1948, *The History of the Persian Empire*, University of Chicago Press, pp.279-280

Ouseley, Sir William, 1823, *Travels to Various Countries of the East, more particularly Persia*, 3 volumes, Rodwell and Martin, London

Phillips, T. J., 1947, Occurrence of the Waxwing in Baluchistan, in *Journal of the Bombay National History Society*, 1946-7, p.160

Pocock, R. I., 1932, The Skin of a Persian Panther (Panthera pardus saxicolor), in *Journal of the Bombay National History Society*, Vol.33, p.211

Roomi, S. M., 1975, *Masnavi Manavi*, Toulou Press, Tehran, Iran

Ross Cockrill, W., 1984, Water Buffalo, in *Evolution of Domesticated Animals*, ed. I. L. Mason, Longman, New York

Ryder, M. L. 1984, Sheep, in *Evolution of Domesticated Animals*, ed. I. L. Mason, Longman, New York

Safa, Z., 1960, *Gang-i-soxan*, Vol. 1, Ibne-Sina Press, Tehran

Saggs, H. W. F., 1984, *The Might That Was Assyria*, Sigwick and Jackson Ltd., London, pp.166-170

Scarce, J., 1989, Tiles, in *The Arts of Persia*, ed. R. W. Ferrier, Yale University Press, New Haven and London

Scullard, H. H., 1974, *The Elephant in the Greek and Roman World*, Thames and Hudson, London

Shahin, D., 1969, Rahian-e-sher-e Emrouz, in Today's Poets, Anastoo Publications, Tehran

Smidt, M., 1986, Elephants, in *Zoo and Wild Animal Medicine*, ed. M. E. Fowler, 2nd Edition, Saunders, Philadelphia, p.889-890

Stevens, R., 1961, Pigeon Towers, p.61, in *The Land of the Great Sophy*, 2nd Edition, Methuen and Co. Ltd, London

Sykes, E. C., 1910, *Persia and its People*, Methuen and Co. Ltd., London

Thesiger, W. 1984, *The Marsh Arabs*, Longman, London

Ticehurst, C. B., Cox, P., Cheesman, R. E., 1930, Birds of the Persian Gulf Islands, in *Journal of the Bombay National History Society*, 1946-7, p.691

Ullens de Schooten, 1964, *M-T. Lords of the Mountains*, Chatto and Windus Ltd.

Welch, S. C., 1976, *Royal Persian Manuscripts*, Thames and Hudson, London

Welland, J., 1977, *Samarkand and Beyond – History of Desert Caravans*, Constable, London

Van Gennep, L., 1949, *Introduction to Le Tapis*, by A. Achdjian, Editions Self, Paris, pp.16-23 (English and French)

SUGGESTED FURTHER READING

1. 1989, *The Arts of Persia*, ed. R. W. Ferrier, Yale University Press, New Haven & London

2. F. Hué, R. D. Etchcopar, 1970, *Les Oiseaux du Proche et du Moyen Orient,* editions Boubée et Cie, Paris

3. Eileen Humphreys, 1991, *The Royal Road, A Popular History of Iran,* Scorpion Publishing, London.

4. David Morgan, 1986, *The Mongols,* Basil Blackwell, Oxford.

5. Robin Lane Fox, 1973, *Alexander the Great,* Futura Publications Ltd, London.

6. J. M. Cook, 1983, *The Persian Empire,* Chaucer Press, Bungay, Suffolk.

7. J. M. Edington and M.A. Edington, 1986, *Ecology Recreation and Tourism,* Cambridge University Press.

DEVON HOUSE
FAMILIES

ENID SHIELDS

with a foreword by
Rt. Hon. Edward Seaga PC, MP

IAN RANDLE PUBLISHERS LIMITED
KINGSTON

A Green Island Press Book

First published 1991 by
Ian Randle Publishers Limited
206 Old Hope Road, Kingston 6, Jamaica

© 1991 Enid Shields

NATIONAL LIBRARY OF JAMAICA CATALOGUING IN
PUBLICATION DATA
Shields, Enid
Devon House Families
Ill.
1. Family & Jamaica   2. Stiebel family   3. Melhado
family
4. Lindo family   5. Devon House (Kingston, Jamaica)
I. Title
929.2'097292
ISBN 976-8100-02-8

CONTENTS

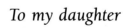
To my daughter

FOREWORD

by

Rt. Hon. Edward Seaga, PC, MP
Leader of the Opposition

The historical record of developing countries, particularly those of the African Diaspora, are usually oral, not monumental. Jamaica is rich in a legacy of both. Over 100 plantation houses from the days when sugar was 'king' are monumental symbols of an historical period of Jamaican plantocracy.

These monuments are known as 'Great Houses', although many of them would be unnoticed today even if they were in good condition. Some were, of course, grandiose and would still be considered 'great houses' today. Rose Hall, Roaring River, Barrett Hall and what is left of Colbeck, are among the better known on this scale.

Some were infamous. Rose Hall and Colbeck, in particular, are steeped in legends of withcraft, barbarity and romance.

Devon House is quite different. It was not built on a plantation but was originally a church property. In fact, by the standards of antiquity, it is quite new having been constructed in the latter part of the last century. But it was built to serve the same purpose as the others, to create an imposing symbol of success and status.

Located less than a mile from the capital of suburban Kingston, Half-Way-Tree, George Stiebel built Devon House after he returned to Jamaica from a sojourn in Venezuela where he was successful in business ventures, particularly, gold mining.

Devon House inspired two other magnificent homes at opposite corners of the intersection at which it was sited. One of these, Abbey Court, was purchased, demolished and developed as one of the first condominium apartment buildings in Jamaica. Abbey Court did not have any particular architectural or historical merit. Devon House was more architecturally important and imposing.

In 1965, another set of 'developers' were poised to strike again. This time it was the Devon House property which was to be purchased and demolished to make way for another condominium. It was Devon House that inspired the construction of the Abbey Court house. Now it was the Abbey Court condominium that was to inspire the demolition and 'development' of Devon House as condominium apartments.

As minister of Development and Welfare at the time with responsibility for cultural affairs, I learned of this plan and immediately issued an interim preservation notice under the National Trust Act which prevented the destruction. It was later purchased by the government to be preserved as an historical monument.

One of the partners in the developer group which was to have erected the condominium, a United States congressman, soon after met me at a New York promotion for the Montego Freeport Development for which I was the guest speaker. He confronted me with the familiar accusatory ring of frustrated interests accustomed to imposing power. 'You people down there don't want development.' I replied, 'Yes, but our style, not yours.'

I had no idea at the time of purchase what we would do with Devon House. I did know instinctively that it should not be demolished. Old homes are costly to maintain, and governments in developing countries generally put a low priority on such matters.

One Sunday morning, it occurred to me that the Devon House could be developed into a showpiece with the out buildings used for culinary and craft operations. I consulted with John Pringle, then Director of Tourism, and with Sergio Dello Strollogo, a consultant to the government's craft development programme who had been provided by the United Nations Development Programme.

As I outlined the tourism implications for a one-stop location to sample our antiques, craft work, food and drink, John Pringle was quick, as usual to realise the potential. Sergio was a man of extraordinary talent who easily understood the other half of the concept, to recreate a symbol of the past in an ambiance which Jamaicans could enjoy.

Restoration and construction was entrusted to Tom Concannon, an English architect, then at the Town Planning Department, who had an excellent feel for the architecture of the period. Sergio worked on the furnishings and newly designed craft items which were later to set the stage through production by Things Jamaican Ltd. for a new wave of design in the craft industry. Devon House was the outlet, Things Jamaican the producer. Both were government entities.

Much of the antique furnishings were actually reproductions being produced by Things Jamaican which led one workman to explain the delay in the scheduled completion date by the observation that 'the antiques dem don' done mek yet.'

The concept of Devon House, as I envisaged it, was not fully developed in the 1960s. More work was done in the 1980s to add other features which, despite some controversy, have made the complex more attractive and popular while retaining its essential ambiance and character. Still more work remains to be done, at another time, to provide other complementary facilities.

A word about the objective of this book is in order. The idea of seeing history through the experiences of families who built great houses in Jamaica is an excellent means of reaching back into the past in a humanised way. Much of Jamaica's colourful history could emerge from research and writing on this far too little known period of our history.

I hope Mrs Enid Shields, the author, will go on to do similar works on other great houses – Colbeck, Barrett Hall, Roaring River, Seville to name a few which are indeed worthy, but forgotten.

Edward Seaga
May 3, 1991

CHAPTER 1

The Rectors

In the late nineteenth century the corner of Trafalgar Road and Hope Road was known as 'Millionaire's Corner'. Here three of the richest men in the island of Jamaica had built mansions. In 1881 George Stiebel built his magnificent 'Devon House'. Not to be outdone the Verleys, owners of the largest bakery in Jamaica, built 'Abbey Court', an imposing three-storied house, while Daniel Finzi, a wine and spirit merchant built 'Reka Dom', which today houses the YMCA. Abbey Court fell by the developer's hand and is replaced by the Abbey Court apartments. But George Stiebel's Devon House was the most beautiful and is today enjoyed by thousands of Jamaicans and visitors alike.

However, the early history of Devon Penn, as it was previously called, was far removed from rich merchants and commerce. In 1655 Britain captured Jamaica from Spain and by the time of the Restoration of Charles II many English families had settled in the island. A specific duty of the governors of Jamaica was to provide religious instruction for the citizens of the island. To the Bishop of London fell the task of selecting the clergymen. The Rev Mr John Zellers, a Swiss, was one of the five ministers of religion selected for service in Jamaica. At a meeting of the island's council at Port Royal he had the good fortune to be recommended 'for the parish of St Andrew' which the governor, Sir Thomas Lynch, described as 'the pleasantest part of the island.'

The glebe, as land attached to the Anglican Church was termed, was given by Charles II by letters patent on 6 May 1667 to 'John Zellers, his heirs, assigne all ye land, meadow, pasture and woodlands...ye same containing 600 acres...together with all edifices, woods, trees, rents, commodities, ways and passages ...and all mines and minerals whatsoever in ye premises.' The exception however was the ownership of gold and silver mines which, if discovered, would be the property of the crown. A yearly rental of 'one penny for every acre now planted and manured...' was all that was required of the minister, but should there be danger of 'insurrection or foreign invasion' Rev Mr John Zellers and his heirs would be required to bear arms in the king's cause upon command of the governor of the island.

Devon Penn was part of the 600 acres granted to John Zellers. The patent however ought not to have been inscribed in the name of Zellers and his heirs as the glebe land was rightly parish property for the use of succeeding parsons.

In 1670, thirteen years after the patent had been granted the vestry suddenly realized the error that had been made. Fortunately John, and later his wife Anne, agreed to sign over their rights to the church wardens of the parish.

The glebe land stretched from the site of the St Andrew Parish Church of Half Way Tree, north to Sandy Gully, encompassing Old Church Road on the east and including the grounds of the present King's House. On the southern side it bordered on Trafalgar Penn, which is now the residence of the British High Commissioner. Although in other parishes newly appointed ministers had to hold their services in the homes of parishioners until churches were eventually built, very early in John's ministry a church was erected for him on the triangular piece of land known today as Old Burial Ground, bordered by Upper Waterloo Road and West Kings House Road. Near this church stood the rectory. But this early church was destroyed, probably blown down by a hurricane, and was replaced by a new church to the north west which was described in 1682 in a letter from Sir Thomas Lynch to the Bishop of London as 'an ordinary Church and pretty parsonage house.'

Although this new church was more substantially built than the first church, it was to last for only six years, as the earthquake of 1692 which caused two-thirds of the town of Port Royal to be swallowed by the sea, also destroyed this church on the Liguanea Plains. On 5 July 1692 we learn from the vestry minutes that undaunted, the vestry ordered 'a new church to be forthwith built . . . and a house for the Minister.' But they did decide to change the site to the present one at Half Way Tree. Originally this cross roads was known as 'Deadman's bones' but it finally took its name from a gigantic cotton tree, a well-known land mark since the time of the conquest of Jamaica.

On 9 April 1672, eight years after his appointment to the Parish Church of St Andrew, John married Anne Struys. She is described in the register as being of 'foreign origin'. The following year, Anne

St Andrew Parish Church – first constructed on this site in 1700, then part of the Devon Penn.

gave birth to her first child. With a growing family John must have found it hard to make two ends meet on his stipend of £100 per annum but the problem was compounded in 1677 when he was forced to petition for his salary. In a letter he writes, 'Notwithstanding His Majesty's recommendation to the Bishop of London to pay £100 in arrears he refused to do so.' The records do not tell us what was the outcome, but we can only hope that John did eventually receive what was owing to him. Luckily he was allowed to augment his salary by charging a fee for baptisms and marriages. His first baptism was on 10 June 1666, and for thirty-six years he faithfully kept the records of all the baptisms, marriages and burials of his parishioners.

John and his wife were married for eighteen years and had six children of whom two sons and three daughters survived infancy. On 1 March 1690 tragedy struck the family when Anne the youngest, aged 4 died, and three days later John lost his wife Anne. This left him the sole parent of four lively teenagers, ranging from the eldest Dorothy, aged 19 to the youngest Henry aged 10.

They were probably still living at the rectory at Old Church Road. Some of the glebe land would have been provision grounds for the rectory and some pasture for the cattle and horses. The rector's slaves would have worked their own provision grounds, as each household had to be a miniature farm, and on that farm all the food needed for the family and workers had to be provided. There would have been poultry, ducks and pigeons and not to be forgotten, pigs. The bacon would have been smoked over open fires not unlike the brick fireplace to be seen at today's Devon House.

John survived his wife by ten years, experiencing the earthquake of 1692 and living to see the new Parish Church completed at Half Way Tree in 1700. Although the vestry minutes had mentioned the building of a 'House for the Minister' we know that one was not built until many years later at Devon Penn. This well loved rector administered to his parish until his death in 1700. The governor of the island described him as an 'esteemed sober honest man.' Between the years 1700 to 1747 four ministers were rectors at the new Parish Church: John Moodie 1700–1710, George Wright 1710–1714, John Cary 1714–1738 and Alexander Inglis 1738–1747. Except that they were all well-educated men, we know little of their activities.

There appears to be no record of the 'house for the minister' after 1692 until 1748 when we find information in the Bishop of London's papers in the Lambeth Palace archives in an 'Act for erecting and repairing of churches in the parish of St Andrew.' If there was no home for the rector the vestry was empowered to rent one at a rental not exceeding £50 per annum, but if this was not possible they were empowered to 'buy or build one providing the building does not exceed the value of £600.' It is reasonable to presume that it was after this that the Devon Penn rectory was built.

Rev Mr George Eccles became rector of the Parish Church between 1747–1760 so he could have been the first clergyman to live at the Devon Penn rectory and certainly his successor Rev Mr Gideon Castlefranc would have occupied it when he became rector in 1760.

We get a vivid picture of Gideon in the 'poems' of Bryan Edwards, the historian, in which he satirizes the rector: 'This Divine was remarkable corpulent, and in the science of good eating was probably better grounded than Apicius of old.' From this poem we gather that he liked turtle feasts and shoulder of wild boar. It had to be stewed for twelve hours and was highly spiced and served up in madeira wine. He was rosy cheeked and boasted a jowl as well as a paunch. The newly-built kitchens at Devon House must have been busy, as undoubtedly Gideon was a gourmet.

He evidently had family in Jamaica, a brother named Smart and a sister named Margaret. We also read of a Castelfranc, a planter of St James, and there was a Peter Castlefranc in London styled 'jeweller', though there appears to be some doubt as to whether he was the father of our goodly Gideon or another brother.

By the time that Gideon served at the Parish Church a great

many slaves had been imported from Africa to work on the plantations. As early as 1696 the Anglican Church had taken an interest in the baptism of these slaves. The government also ordered in its slave code that 'All masters, mistresses, owners and employers are to endeavour as much as possible the instruction of their slaves in the principles of the Christian religion....'

The rosy-cheeked Gideon appears to be the first rector of the parish who was interested in the religious instruction of these slaves. He was 'very zealous in the baptism of slaves.' They were often baptised en bloc but there were difficulties, as the Assembly fixed the fee for a slave baptism at £1 3s 9d which did not encourage the planters to have their slaves baptised. And as the vestry members were made up of the planter class it was hard for the rectors to go against their wishes as they controlled the church funds.

In a letter to the Bishop of London we read, 'Mr Castlefranc being unable to send a report asked John Venn to do so as for propagating the christian religion amongst these poor creatures tho' it was most earnestly to be desired yet it seems to be attended with insuperable difficulties.' He relates that masters would not give their slaves time to attend instruction. When he himself attempted to baptise 'a sensible well inclined slave' the slave refused baptism as that meant that he would not be able to go to any dances nor have any 'antic ceremonies about his grave,...and to deprive the slaves of their funeral rites by burning was to them a punishment greater than death itself.' The letter goes on to tell us that the freed slaves and mulattoes were all baptised and attended church regularly.

In spite of these difficulties the rotund Gideon continued his baptism of slaves at the Parish Church for another eight years. But with his intemperate style of living at the Devon Penn rectory it is not surprising that he died early. Cundall tells us that he was interred 'with his family inside the rails of the altar and to the north part of the communion table' in April 1768.

The Rev Mr John Poole succeeded Gideon as minister of the Parish Church and he was to fare well financially as within a year the Assembly passed an act ordering that the stipend of the clergy be raised from £100 to £420 per annum. This was a considerable rise but long overdue, as it was the first increase in one hundred years and the vestry minutes of 1781 record 'fees for burial without doors, ten shillings, within the Church £10, within the rails of the altar £20.'

One of this rector's last acts was to add his name to the list of vestry members who congratulated Admiral Rodney when he arrived in the island in 1782, after his victory over the French navy under Admiral de Grasse. There was great jubilation all over the island as through all of the wars of the eighteenth century the inhabitants of Jamaica lived under fear of a French attack.

In the vestry minutes we find John being given £50 in lieu of parsonage so either the Devon Penn rectory had been rented or it was being repaired. In another entry he acquainted the justices and the vestry that he had 'decided to leave shortly on a voyage to England without the intent of returning and was desirous of being succeeded in the rectory of St Andrew by the Rev Mr John Campbell whom he recommended. This was unanimously approved.'

We read in the Fulham papers, that 'John Campbell was given £20 passage money and he had to within the space of three months convey himself by vessel to Jamaica.' He arrived in the island in 1782. He was 33 when he became the rector of St Andrew. The vestry minutes tell us that the minister was 'now in possession of the glebe lands and he was to be paid all rents by tenants.' But he had promised to 'accept no consideration money for granting leases of the glebe lands.'

With a name like Campbell and a graduate of St Andrew we can presume that he was a Scotsman. On 21 May 1780 he had been ordained a priest by the Bishop of Litchfield and Coventry at St George's, Bloomsbury, London.

On his arrival he was given £50 in lieu of parsonage and this allowance continued for sometime, so he and his wife and five year old son Alexander had to live in rented houses, as evidently the Devon Penn rectory was in a state of bad repair. In fact when they moved into the rectory John had to repair the old house and he wrote to the vestry 'requesting some further repairs and additions to the rectory and stating that he himself had laid out money thereon and that he had no objection to bear a reasonable proportion.' A committee examined the matter and in 1787 an exciting report reads:

> the following repairs and additions and alterations to be necessary for the convenience of the rector. The Piazza to be venetioned, the upper sliding and the lower with fixed blinds and two double doors, the one at the westward and the other in front, the whole to be painted green. A guttering is wanted around the house for the purpose of collecting rain water. A new stable with coach house 40 feet long and 18 wide in the clear . . . the three front windows that are in the upstairs dormitory require shutters and the broken glass to be repaired. The walls of the passage to one of the rooms have sunk, and the plaster in consequence much defaced and wants repairs. Your committee to observe on the last two repairs that when the rector entered into possession of the house these walls and plasters were new . . . Six feet in the back from the new room to the west end of the house to be repaired and a gutter is wanted to carry off the water which in heavy rains gather and stand and will eventually . . . the foundations of the whole. Your committee beg further to recommend to the vestry the erection of another building of two rooms one above the other underneath at the back of the present staircase to stand either on arch pillars 20 feet by 16 in the clear, signed S. Marshall Alexander Richie.

The committee agreed to have the report carried out but ordered that the costs should not exceed £1000 and should be paid to the rector as soon as the vestry was satisfied that 'the sum has been properly and judiciously expended.'

From this report we can picture the rectory, a gabled red brick two-storied house with all the woodwork and jalousies painted green. There is also an estate map in the National Library dated 1788 which shows the present site of Devon House marked 'Rev Campbell's Devon Penn.' By 1960 this early history of Devon Penn had long been forgotten and the story went that the history of Devon House had started with the building of Devon House in 1881 by George Stiebel. But when in 1960, Tom Concannon, the architect, was restoring the building he suspected that this was not the case and reported: 'It is likely that the coach house (west) and the silver vaults near the coach house date from an earlier house . . . a room now connected to the main house, used in recent years as a swimming pool . . . suggest that the unit was not planned with the Stiebel construction of 1881.'

In March 1987 two hundred years after the vestry minutes were written we find another architect, Mr Cox, reporting: 'The bath house in relation to the main house strongly suggest those predated the Stiebel house. The brick work of the coach house and external wall to the west of the present court yard, (or parking ground) the only wall to be built in English bond which became unfashionable in the eighteenth century in England, together with the two cook houses, suggest that these might date from the late eighteenth century or early nineteenth century.'

From our latest research we know that both Tom's and Mr Cox's suspicions were perfectly correct. Part of today's Grog Shoppe is that coach house which was built in 1787 and mentioned in the vestry minutes and as no repairs had been mentioned for the kitchens, these could have dated from the mid-eighteenth century when the rectory was first built. Many years ago J. H. Campbell, a well-known lawyer, said that George Stiebel built Devon House on the foundations of the St Andrew Parish Church rectory, and certainly, today, there are cellars to be seen under Devon House.

But the mystery of Devon House is the vault. Did this predate even the first rectory? With a puzzled face Mr Cox said, 'It is built

The Vault: Did this building predate even the first rectory? Today 'The Vault' is a jewellery shop.

more strongly than Giddy House at Port Royal which was used for storing ammunition,' and Ray McIntyre, who worked with Tom Concannon on the restoration, tells us that the vault has a double skin which means it has complete inner walls and is lined with metal inside. We ask ourselves why would the church want such a strong room? A visiting Canadian military man said that he had seen similar buildings in other parts of the Caribbean which had been used for storing ammunition. But the pages of history have not yet solved the problem, so the mystery remains.

John Campbell and his family were to occupy the rectory for the next thirty or so years. After the repairs and additions had been completed we can be sure that the Campbells had a very comfortable parsonage in which to reside and they obviously owned a carriage. Devon Penn was still surrounded by hundreds of acres of the glebe and it still functioned as a rural farm. It was here that the young Alexander grew up, and while his father attended his clerical duties, his mother supervised her staff in the same kitchen that we see behind the Grog Shoppe, which is now part of the restaurant.

In March 1806 we find him writing to the bishop on the conditions of the clergy in Jamaica. He does not recommend it to anyone who has any prospect of preferment in England. 'Although the public services are confined to two on Sunday, local custom requires baptisms, marriages and funerals to be held from private homes which increases the minister's labour.' Although John found this duty tiresome he was very interested in the army and he devoted a lot of time to the British soldiers at Up Park Camp, now occupied by the Jamaica Defence Force. During his rectorship there were a large number of military baptisms and marriages recorded, and some of the soldiers stationed as far away as Fort Clarence attended his services.

He also baptised many slaves. In 1790 it is recorded that at Vale Royal five slaves belonging to Simon Taylor, one of the richest men in the island, were baptised. Simon was one of John's parishioners. The rector appears to have been a humane man interested in helping the slaves, for we find him submitting to the consideration of the vestry, 'that a certain portion of the church yard be selected...for burying such christian slaves...that such persons of colour in Kingston as were born in the parish and whose families and relatives have been buried on either of the church yards in the parish should be entitled to that privilege.' He also introduced the practice of preaching a special sermon at the evening service directed to the less educated members of the parish. 'There are many who are in ignorance of the faith but are willing to be instructed,' he wrote to the bishop.

He received the honour of becoming the senior member of His Majesty's Commissioners who were appointed to exercise ecclesiastical jurisdiction and later he became chaplain to the council and was presented with a 'silver chalice, flagon and waiter gilt with gold and two plain silver waiters.'

John served for thirty-one years as rector of the St Andrew

Parish Church until he died in his sixty-fourth year. His long journeys on horseback to baptise, marry and bury many of his parishioners had probably had an adverse effect on his health.

He was evidently well loved by his parishioners as a monument to his memory is still to be seen on the north wall of the Parish Church, 'Sacred to the memory of the Rev John Campbell who departed this life in London, 30th Oct. 1813 aged 64. The justices and the vestry have caused this monument to be erected as a tribute to his merit and exemplary good conduct....'

His son Alexander Campbell succeeded him as rector of the St Andrew Parish Church.

To Alexander the rectory was very much home, here he had grown to manhood and he was sent to Scotland to finish his education. He attained his MA at Edinburgh University, and in 1803 he was ordained a priest by the Bishop of London at Fulham Palace. He then returned to Jamaica and became rector of the Kingston Parish Church in 1805 were he remained until his father's

Alexander Campbell served as rector of St. Andrew Parish Church for forty five (45) years!

death in 1813. It was during this time that he met Ann Mitchell McGlashan, the eldest daughter of Dr McGlashan, whom he married in 1809 when he was 32.

In 1812 while his father was living at the Devon Penn rectory the baptismal records of the St Andrew Parish Church register a son born to Alexander and Ann Campbell on 11 September. This baby was 1 year old when Alexander returned to live at the parsonage that he knew so well. In 1816 another son Andrew William was born at Devon Penn. In that same year they were to lose their 4-year-old son Charles and the newly-born baby Andrew must have been a comfort to the grief-stricken parents. Two years later they had another son whom they christened Charles after his dead brother. Charles was later to become a medical doctor. Three years later another baby Duncan Houston was born at the rectory on 12 March 1821. With an increasing family it was lucky for Ann that her father-in-law had requested additions to the rectory. It was here many years later in 1878 that Duncan Houston was to die. He was one of the few people whom we know was born and died at Devon Penn. Alexander served for forty-five years as rector of the Parish Church and resided at the Devon Penn rectory.

During these years he must have had a busy time bringing up his young family and attending to his priestly duties. He succeeded his father as senior commissary appointed to exercise ecclesiastical jurisdiction. He was also made Dean of the county of Surrey and as rector of St Andrew Parish Church he automatically became Dean of rural St Andrew and he was Chaplain-General of the British Forces. It must have been happy days at Devon Penn with Ann and Alexander surrounded by their growing family; they all reached maturity at the old house and they would have been pleased when the youngest Duncan became a deacon, following in his father's and grandfather's footsteps.

The long-lived Alexander worked almost to the end of his life as the last baptismal register entry signed by him was on 4 November 1858 and he died on 8 December 1858. His memorial tablet can be seen in the Parish Church: 'This tablet is erected by friends and parishioners in memory of the late Alexander Campbell … universally respected and loved.' His wife outlived him by fifteen years and his daughter Mrs Bowerbank gave the church a portrait of her father which was hung in the vestry. A brass chandelier was also given to the church in memory of himself and his wife.

In his will Alexander appointed his three sons John, Charles and Duncan as trustees and he left all his 'real and personal estate to his dear wife Ann.'

Between the years 1858 to 1872 three more rectors served the Parish Church and in 1872 Alexander's son Duncan was appointed rector. He was already an archdeacon and was now 51 and well into middle age. He was as far as we know the only rector of the Parish Church up until then who had been born in Jamaica and was a Jamaican. Once more he found himself living at Devon Penn rectory which to him, was an old family home.

For many years the archdeacon had been rector of Kingston and during this period he had married Emily, daughter of A. G. Spencer, Bishop of Jamaica. She was as full of good works as her husband and we read of her founding an orphanage on the site of 'Reka Dom'. She would have found it conveniently placed as she could walk over from the rectory to inspect its progress.

The archdeacon and Enos Nuttall, later Bishop of Jamaica, wrote *Suggestions for the better selecting, preparing and appointing the Catechists of the Church of England in Jamaica and remarks on honorary lay readers*, published in 1869. Like most Victorian gentlemen the archdeacon was a trifle verbose. Apart from his literary ambitions, Duncan had a burning desire to restore and beautify the old familiar church which he had attended from the days when he was a toddler.

In 1872, the year that the archdeacon became rector of St Andrew Parish Church, the capital of Jamaica was moved from Spanish Town to Kingston, and the governors now lived at King's

*Duncan Houston Campbell – first Jamaican born rector
of the St. Andrew Parish church.*

House which had been Bishop's Lodge and part of the glebe. They
worshipped at the St Andrew Parish Church, so it became
fashionable for the social set and the officials to attend the church
which the governor honoured. With the church's growing
importance the archdeacon was anxious to see his cherished dream
of restoration come true, but he was destined to disappointment as
he was to be rector for only six years, when he died at the age of 57.

There is a brass plaque in the porch, 'To the Glory of God and
the loving memory of Emily Pembroke wife of the late venerable
Archdeacon Campbell, a chime of bells was erected in this tower by
members of the congregation and other friends. Easter 1889.' In the
west porch also we see an inscription, 'This porch is offered to the

house of the Lord in memory of two brothers, the beloved physician Charles Campbell and the dear Archdeacon Duncan Houston Campbell.'

All the Campbells, father, son and grandson, were obviously very popular with their parishioners. The family after living on and off at the Devon Penn rectory for nearly one hundred years was finally to leave and the old rectory was not long to survive their departure.

In 1879 Rev Mr Hubert H. Isaac, MA became rector of the Parish Church. He was born in London in 1835. When he was quite young his parents brought him to Jamaica. The Isaac family had evidently had property in the island for some time as the historian Cundall tells us that on arrival, 'they went to the original family residence "Iver" in St Elizabeth.' How long he stayed in Jamaica we do not know, but we do know that he returned to England to finish his education.

When he became rector of the Parish Church Hubert was inspired with his predecessor's dream of remodelling the building which had been built during the rectorship of the Rev Mr John Zellers. To him fell the task of restoring the church which is much the same as the one we see today at Half Way Tree. He was enthusiastic about the work and he was referred to as the 'enlightened and indefatigable rector.'

Hubert served as rector of the Parish Church for twenty-one years before he died in 1900. He was the last rector to live at the Devon Penn rectory where he resided for less than a year as in October 1879 'the lay body of the Church of England' sold Devon Penn to George Stiebel.

CHAPTER 2

George Stiebel

George Stiebel bought the Devon Penn rectory and lands from the Church of England in 1879 and built Devon House on its foundations in 1881. He and his family lived there until 1923.

George Stiebel's life reads like a fairy tale. He was born about 1821, the son of a Jamaican housekeeper and a German Jew. George was eventually to surmount the handicap of his humble birth and rise to a position of responsibility and respect in the island. No record of his baptism has been found but his father, whom the family refer to as Daniel, was more than likely Sigismund Daniel Stiebel, who was naturalized in 1823. He had a brother named Bernard who had also been naturalized. The brothers set up a ships' chandler's business in Kingston. They had come to Jamaica from London where the Stiebels had a banking business. The family tradition is that the Stiebels originally came from Hamburg, Germany.

Family tradition also reveals that Daniel was a very religious and strait-laced man. Dickie Jackson, Daniel's great-great grandson, tells us that Daniel was at first mortified by the arrival of a son to his housekeeper, but George soon endeared himself to his father, who removed him from his mother's quarters and brought him into the main house, where he grew up under his father's strict discipline.

As his son grew older, Daniel sent him to an exclusive private school in Kingston where he could receive a classical education. The other pupils, sons of well-to-do parents, teased young George unmercifully and their parents were incensed, as they considered that he was not of the right social background to attend this school.

At 14 George felt that he could no longer stand the 'ribbing' of the boys at school, and he rebelled and ran away. His father, after some search found him working in a carpenter's yard. 'A carpenter I find you, so a carpenter you shall be,' said the irate parent. George showed a keen interest in shipbuilding, so Daniel apprenticed him to a shipwright. At the end of his apprenticeship his father and uncle employed him at their store in Kingston.

The adventurous George must have found working with his father too dull and by the time that he was 19 he was involved in the reconstruction of Ferry Inn, a well-known and very old inn on the road between Kingston and Spanish Town, where weary travellers from many parts of the country refreshed themselves before coming to Kingston, and where too the horses were often changed.

The *Jamaica Standard* of 5 July 1842 informs us that 'George Stiebel carpenter of 21 Church Lane' was 'balloted for militia service.' Luckily for George his father settled some money on him with which he bought a schooner and started transporting cargo between North and South America. So successful was the enterprise that it was not long before George increased his ships to a fleet of three and expanded his trading to some of the West Indian islands.

In 1844 he heard that the slave population in Cuba had become restive knowing that slavery had been abolished in the nearby island of Jamaica, and had rebelled. George saw a lucrative cargo within sight and he was quick to begin gun-running to the rebel slaves in the Spanish island. It was not long before this got him into trouble with the Spanish authorities and he was arrested and thrown into a Cuban prison. Undaunted, George made friends with his guard whom he discovered was also a Freemason like himself,

*Charcoal sketch of young
George Stiebel.*

and with his goaler's help he escaped. This put an end to his gun-running adventures.

When he was in his twenties George had fallen in love with Magdalen Baker, daughter of a Moravian missionary. But his escapade in Cuba had not improved his image in the eyes of her parents, so when he asked her to marry him they refused to allow their daughter to enter into this union. The young couple were determined to wed, but Magdalen's parents remained adamant that there was to be no marriage with this adventurous young man of small fortune and unacceptable parentage.

Magdalen was reluctant to disobey her parents so they waited many years until after her mother and father died, and so it was not until about 1851 that they were at last married.

Their first born was a son, Sigismund, named after his grandfather. Two years later a girl was born and was christened Theresa. They had been married for five years and Sigismund was 4 years old when all George's ships ran into a terrible storm and were lost at sea. George himself was aboard one of the schooners which sank off the coast of Venezuela, but luckily he was able to swim ashore. He had the foresight to put all his money in a leather belt which he fastened around his waist and, half-drowned, he struggled to the shore.

He must have been distraught when he realized that he had lost everything, but George was not one to accept defeat. With the little money he had rescued he bought goods and became a peddlar. He saved every penny that he made and bought himself a mule. He travelled from Caracas to Maracaibo and discovered that transporting gold was very profitable.

He even went as far south as El Callo, and as he made money he bought himself a team of mules. But it was a long journey for the animals and at that time, about 1857, when George was in his thirties, Venezuela was plagued with bandits in the country areas. The robbers were constantly capturing his mules and the cargo they carried. Ingeniously he thought of a solution; he bought grain and fed his mules on this, rather than on grass. Soon his animals were outrunning the bandits' grass-fed mules. He also armed his drivers and so they were able to out-run and out-shoot the robbers.

George's profits rose as he succeeded in his dealings with buying gold and transporting it to Caracas. He had now become fascinated with the glittering stuff and dreamt of making his fortune. By this time he had gained an insight into the mining of gold, and when he heard that the Venezuelan government was interested in leasing an old mine, El Callo, George persuaded eleven of his friends to become partners. He put all his capital into the business, but for a time the mine seemed to have been 'worked out.' When some of his partners lost heart George bought them out, and in a short time he owned five of the twelve shares. He lived frugally, and with determination worked day and night to rediscover the gold vein. There must have been many times when he felt utterly down-hearted, but he would not give up until he found gold. This he did, and to this day his great-grandson, Richard Jackson, treasures a stone of quartz with a gold vein running through it which came from the El Callo mine.

One can imagine the celebrations that must have taken place after so long a search. With hard work he operated the mine successfully. He was now on his way to making a fortune but the gold mining needed his personal attention to ensure its continued growth and he stayed in Venezuela until it was producing profitably.

George Stiebel was to remain in Venezuela for fifteen years. Many believed that he had abandoned his wife Magdalen, but this was not so. He sent money for her whenever he could, through Leopold Schloss, the son of one of Daniel Stiebel's partners, and a friend of the Stiebel family, who had always looked after George's affairs when he was away from Jamaica. Leopold was also commissioned to buy property for him in Jamaica.

Nonetheless, Magdalen must have had a very trying time. She had been left the task of raising a boy of 4 and a girl of 2. At first when he did not return she would not have known if George was dead or alive. Many years later her only son fell ill and he died as it were on the threshold of life. He was buried at the Methodist Church called Ebenezer in Kingston. The inscription on his tomb reads, 'Sigismund James Stiebel died on 7th November, 1871 aged 19.' It must have been heartbreaking for the grass widow who now only had Theresa aged 17.

Whether George knew of his son's death before he returned to Jamaica we do not know, but certainly he was overjoyed to be reunited in 1873 with his beloved wife and daughter. He was now a very wealthy man, but the story goes that in Venezuela an Indian woman had put a curse on him that none of his family would live to enjoy his wealth. As far as curses go, if you believe in them, the family did have a lot of misfortune. On arrival, he upbraided his wife when he found her in a modest house. When he asked her what she had done with all the money that he had sent her, she replied, 'Put it in the bank.'

'That money was to make you and Theresa comfortable,' he admonished, 'Why didn't you buy a bigger house?'

*A more mature
George Stiebel.*

'It wouldn't have been right, George, for me to live extravagantly,' she replied. 'Remember, I was a grass widow and it would not have been seemly for me to attract attention to myself and Theresa.' George was to put this right and in no uncertain way, from then on he lavished money on them. He was now 52 and after his long struggle he was going to enjoy the fruits of his labour.

He decided that Theresa should go to a finishing school in France. He took Magdalen and Theresa to England and bought a house in Wimpole Street, where many West Indian families had had houses since the eighteenth century. It was then a very fashionable part of London and he furnished the house lavishly. A carriage and a pair of horses were bought by George who always held that 'commoners never drive four in hand; that must be left for the gentry!' He also made sure that he possessed the best pair of horses that were to be had in England. When George took his wife and daughter touring in Europe they did so in grand style. Not only did the carriage and English coachman cross the Channel with the family, but also an English ladies' maid as well as a cook.

Rare portrait of Magdalen Stiebel.

George's friend, Leopold Schloss, advised him to sell some of his mining shares to the Verleys of Abbey Court and invest in property in Jamaica. George commissioned him to purchase the properties. Two sugar estates, Lloyds and Retreat, were bought along with a wharf at Church Street, Great Salt Pond and a coffee property called Mullet, and a cattle pen, Minard, in St Ann. All these properties lost money except Great Salt Pond in St Catherine. George probably had quite enough money already from his gold mine without having to worry too much with the management of the estates or maybe he was not interested in farming. The lovely old great house at Minard set in rolling pastures was to become a happy summer home for the family for three generations to come.

George's ability and generosity were soon recognized in Jamaica and he was invited to sit on many boards. He was a member of the Board of Education and also Gas Commissioner (at that time there was piped gas for lighting throughout Kingston). He was also on the board of directors of the Jamaica Co-operative Fruit Insurance Company, the Jamaica Permanent Benefit Society and the Kingston Sailors' Home, as well as chairman of the Parochial Board and of the Kingston and St Andrew Union Poorhouse. He was beloved by many, a highly respected and kind man. All through his life he helped people in straightened circumstances, and when thanked his reply was, 'Ah, I was once poor, and I know what it is to be poor and to want!'

It was not long after this that George met Richard Hill Jackson, a solicitor who had lately moved from Spanish Town to Kingston, where he had set up a practice and was steadily building a large clientele. George and Richard liked each other immediately and Richard became a visitor at the Stiebel home at Shortwood Penn.

Richard had been born in 1846 in a house on Ellis Street, Spanish Town, which was the family's main residence. His mother was a Miss Joanna Fuller Aldred and she had brought a dowry of £20 000 with her on her marriage to Thomas, a fair sum in those days. Richard was named after Richard Hill, the famous naturalist, who was a friend of his father, Thomas Witter Jackson, a stipendary magistrate in St Thomas.

As a youngster Richard often accompanied his father when he rode about his business in the parish. After the Morant Bay Rebellion, Thomas, in a report to the Royal Commission sent to investigate the uprising states that 'there were direct acts of oppression.' This was not acceptable to the authorities and Thomas was relieved of his post as magistrate, which was very distressing as the Jacksons had young children to educate. Luckily for Richard he was sent to school in Germany by a wealthy uncle who lived in France. When he finished his education he chose law as a profession, which was not surprising as he had come from a long line of lawyers and judges. When he returned to Jamaica he was articled to the firm of Hill and Airy who were leading solicitors in Spanish Town. On 18 October 1869 he qualified as a lawyer. Later he took over the law firm of the late Mr Jas Allwood. It was stated at the time that Mr Jackson's ability and close attention to his duties soon brought him a lucrative practice which extended throughout the parishes of St Catherine, St John, St Dorothy, St Thomas-ye-Vale and Clarendon. He was most successful in a large number of cases in which he was retained, and his growing practice entailed a great deal of riding to the various courts that he attended.

All went well until the capital of Jamaica was moved in 1872 from Spanish Town to Kingston. This brought about the decline of the old town which had been a very festive city during the meeting of the House of Assembly, when the planters brought their families to their town houses in the capital. After the Morant Bay Rebellion there was no longer a House of Assembly, as Jamaica was then ruled directly by the Crown. With the deterioration of the capital Richard found his clientele dwindling and as a consequence in 1874 he moved to Kingston and there established his law practice.

George and Richard were staunch friends by the time Theresa finished her education in France. She was 21 when she returned to the island, a polished young lady who was described as 'being very dignified.' It soon became obvious that Richard, now a frequent visitor at Shortwood Penn, was in love with the charming Theresa, and he asked her to marry him. George, of course was delighted, but not so the Jackson family, who were up in arms when they heard of the engagement. The Jacksons were considered gentry and the old Jamaican families were strongly opposed to mixed marriages. However, when they realized that she was heiress to a vast fortune their objections were somewhat subdued. The poise and dignity of the bride-to-be may also have played a part in reconciling her fiancé's family.

George wanted no expense spared in the arrangements for the approaching wedding, which was to be a splendid affair. Magdalen and Theresa ordered the bride's trousseau to be made in Paris and commissioned the nuns who had taught Theresa to make all her underclothing of the finest handkerchief linen, all hand-embroidered in exquisite designs. As the day approached George ordered an ox which was to be roasted for the poor of Kingston to celebrate the occasion.

They were a striking couple, he was 33, blue-eyed and blonde and she, 23 and an attractive brunette. They were married in March 1879 at the St Andrew Parish Church. A large crowd gathered at the church gate to watch the wedding, as Richard was already a popular figure and his father-in-law was much loved, especially by the poor of Kingston.

As George had not yet built Devon House the newly-wed couple probably lived with her parents at Shortwood Penn. A year later their first child was born and christened George, after his grandfather.

In the month of October 1879 at 11.30 a.m. the ownership of Devon Penn by the Church of England ended. Men of commerce were to take the place of clerics. George Stiebel and the 'lay body' of the church signed a conveyance selling 'the part of the glebe lands attached to the rectory for the sum of £1500 ... all that piece or parcel of land known by the name of Devon Penn containing 53 acres of land ... dwelling house or all the other houses, buildings, erections and fixtures thereon ... saving and excepting from the said lands 13 acres thereof whereon is to be erected a rectory.' The new rectory was built and today it is part of the Priory School, but for many years it housed the rectors of the Parish Church after the sale of the Devon Penn rectory.

Although a millionaire, George Stiebel bought Devon Penn in partnership with his rich friend Leopold Schloss. Within the boundaries of Devon Penn there were 32 acres called Cashew Penn which had not been included in the original sale. It was not until 2.00 p.m. on 1 April that George signed another conveyance with the church buying 'part of the glebe land attached to the rectory ... subject to an unexpired lease of Mary Dewar the tenant in possession ... convey and confirm George Stiebel and his heirs all those two adjacent parcels of land called Cashew Grove.' George had to pay the tenant compensation for her unexpired lease. 'Mary Dewar the tenant in possession thereof, £300, being consideration money.'

At the age of 60, George now turned his attention to the building of Devon House. The sale completed, he proceeded to pull down the decrepit rectory, which had housed so many rectors of the St Andrew Parish Church. On the foundations he started building his dream house. The actual builder was Charles P. Lazarus. Charles' father was a Lebanese and his mother was of French descent, his grandmother having escaped from Haiti during the revolution. He had attended the Roman Catholic school on Sutton Street and Wolmer's School. Like George, he began working at a very early age, 13, when he started as an engineer with the firm which erected the Kingston and Liguanea Water Works. But Charles had ambition and at the age of 19 he had started a business for himself as an engineer. After working on various sugar estates, he established the West End Foundry in Kingston in 1863. He built up a successful business and in 1870 he did work for Sir Charles Bright on the submarine cable. Like George he was a public spirited man. He served at one time as Mayor of Kingston and on the council. He was on the advisory committee of the Kingston Technical School and later he became a Justice of the Peace.

In spite of all his achievements, Charles was a rough diamond, but most amusing. 'Most anecdotes that are allegedly connected with Lazarus are unprintable.' One story is recounted by Clyde Hoyte which demonstrates what a character the man was. 'Once Lazarus was summoned to give evidence in the Supreme Court and he went into the witness box clad in his every day working overalls (which in those days would have been considered contempt of court). The Judge is alleged to have commented, "Mr Lazarus, I see you have thought fit to come to court in your working garb?" To which Mr Lazarus replied, "With respect, your Honour, I noticed that your Honour also has on working clothes."'

Another delightful anecdote relates that Lazarus once sent the British government a bill for repairs on a Naval ship: 'One stud 6 pence. Total amount for fitting above stud 3 shillings. Total amount for knowing where to fit stud £960.'

Charles Lazarus and George Stiebel started working with great zest on the palatial residence. It was solidly built with red bricks and timber, no expense was spared. The fence of spiked iron rails were set in cement and at the entrance were imposing ornate cast iron gates. These had been imported from Scotland. They had been made in the Sun Foundry by C. E. Smith and Company of Glasgow. The large gates in the centre opened to allow carriages through and the two side gates were for guests on foot. George was to do lavish entertaining and often the many guests had to be dropped at the gates by their coachman, the drive being so crowded with carriages.

The magnificent house was set well back behind palm trees and spreading ancient trees which clustered close and huge dark boulders lay on the green lawns, a reminder of countless years gone by. In the centre of the carriage way, which was wide and curved for ease in turning the carriages, stood a well. Today in its place is a two-tiered fountain of cast iron cherubs and pelicans.

Present day shot of original cast iron gate and spiked iron rails at the entrance of Devon House.

After the building was completed the magnificent days of Devon House began. As the many guests arrived for one of George's parties they were struck by the four life-size classical statues that stood on plinths in the garden in front of the house. These represented the four seasons and George had brought them from Europe. They would have been an unusual sight in Jamaica, reminiscent more of Italy than our colonial houses. Beyond, the guests looked up at the three-storied house. The upstairs was graceful with open balconies in front and on either side. Up the wide white marble steps flanked by a wooden balustrade, the guests streamed all eager to inspect the house which was now the talk of the town. They entered the front portico and walked into the long gallery as they called it in those days, a verandah enclosed by jalousies and windows. The jalousies let in the cooling trade winds but kept out the glare and sun which was harmful to ladies' complexions. The days of sun worship had not yet begun. They entered the drawing room, where ladies would retire after dinner, while men sipped their port. The dining room on the east which is now the drawing room, held a dining table that could seat over twenty. Marble-topped mahogany serving tables, where butlers carved enormous roasts and huge sideboards laden with silver, stood against the walls.

George had brought all the furniture from Europe. While they dined, the high doors were thrown wide-open to the verandah and the night breeze from the mountains kept the ladies cool in their voluminous Victorian dresses. The gentlemen in their tailcoats would have been no less grateful for the cooling effect after a heavy and lavish meal. Food was a very important item in those days of plenty and some of the gentry in Jamaica even had French cooks. On the west was the library. When Sir Joshua Rowe, the Chief Justice died, Richard bought his bookcase of gothic design and there he kept his law books. (His daughter-in-law, Nora Jackson, uses it now at Abbey Court to display some of the precious china, relics of Devon House.) The library also opened on to a verandah.

The Dining Room.

The enclosed gallery at the top of the West Staircase.

Through the archway of the drawing room the staircase rose ahead leading to the first floor and under the staircase was a cupboard where the wines and liquors were kept. A room directly behind the staircase was the butler's serving pantry, and here the waiters brought the steaming dishes from the outside kitchen, for in the days of wood and coal stoves the cooking was always done in a kitchen some distance from the house. The roasts were brought in under large silver dome-shaped covers.

The family breakfasted on the large open verandah at the back of the house which looked out onto a shady garden, brightly coloured by shrubs clustered near the house. Beyond was open land and distant mountains, and as far as the eye could see there were no houses, thus giving a truly rural appearance.

Ascending the staircase on the west of the enclosed front verandah, we come to an enclosed gallery, and from this we can walk onto the open balcony which at that time looked across trees and pastures to Trafalgar Penn. It was from here that George waved to crowds who gathered at the gates to await the announcement of their first grandchild, Magdalen Hilda, who was born at Devon House.

Turning back into the enclosed verandah we enter the ballroom with its ceiling decorated with medallions of cherubs hung from bows and wreaths of flowers. At a glance we would think they were Wedgwood porcelain plaques, but they have been found to be a form of hard plaster painted the Wedgwood blue pattern. From the ceiling hangs the beautiful chandelier that George had brought from Europe. Today it still graces the ballroom and we have to thank the people who painstakingly put it together again from two broken parts of the original chandelier. George brought Louis XV gilded furniture over from France to furnish this room. The long doors of the room were hand-painted with delicate designs. On either side of the long room were two French commodes of marquetry and above them were large gilded mirrors that reached to the ceiling. It was in this room that George and Magdalen entertained hundreds of guests. Many years later one of his great-granddaughters said, 'But it must have been very hot to have all those people in a room without airconditioning.' 'Oh no,' her father, Arthur, told her, 'my grandfather brought a shipload of ice blocks cut from icebergs from Nova Scotia and they were cut to fit into tins which were arranged against the wall of the room and then were covered with banks of flowers, so as to disguise them and as decoration.' It was here that the British Army officers danced until dawn with the young girls of St Andrew. George often entertained the whole regiment on the lawns of Devon House.

To the north of the central staircase was a small, delightful room filled with delicate French gilded furniture which had a hand-painted pattern on each chair. This was Theresa's boudoir and here she did embroidery and wrote letters.

On the east side of the staircase was the master bedroom where George and Magdalen slept. They each had adjoining dressing rooms complete with a bidet for Magdalen and a wash-stand with goblet and basin as well as a commode. A bath tub was brought in when required.

On the west was Theresa and Richard's bedroom and they also had adjoining dressing rooms. The next room to them was a bedroom for the children, who came in quick succession.

One of the first things that George did after building Devon House was to lay out a racecourse at the back of the house stretching to what is now West King's House Road. He then hired young Sam Burke to train the Stiebel horses. He had always loved horses, and like his descendants, never liked to miss a racing meeting. Today his great-grandson's horses still wear the Stiebel colours. He also had tennis courts laid out on the east.

At this time Theresa was busy producing children. In the sixteen years she was married, she had no less than twelve pregnancies, six of which miscarried before birth. The first baby girl Magdalen called Maggie was born at Devon House. In 1884 followed Douglas who looked like his father, blonde and blue-eyed;

Magdalen 'Maggie' Stiebel Jackson – first baby girl born at Devon House.

Gladys was born in 1885; another girl, Amy, followed her; the baby of the family, Arthur, was born in 1891. He was the last child to be born at Devon House.

Theresa and Richard now had six children living at Devon House and an English governess was employed to attend to their training and education. It is said that the marriage was not a happy one. Richard was handsome and charming and had a 'host of friends' so it is not surprising if he did have eyes for the girls, when Theresa was so often incapacitated with her frequent pregnancies. Devon House was noisy with the chatter of children and the playing of the piano. The three girls were taught to sing and play the piano, as no well-bred girl escaped such training at that time, for when they grew up they were expected to sing or play some instrument at parties. It was the days when guests must 'sing for their supper', for there were no radios, television sets or stereos.

Young George was sent to York Castle, a private school for boys in the parish of St Ann. He was good at games, especially tennis, and in the holidays he and his brother Douglas enjoyed watching the horses being trained at Devon House.

On Fridays Theresa and her mother went to market in a pony and trap which was especially kept for this purpose. Both mother and daughter, being excellent caterers, liked to choose their own vegetables.

George and Magdalen, in the evening of their life, were surrounded by all that they could ever desire, their grandchildren, daughter and son-in-law, a beautiful house and George had his racetrack and horses. These were indeed the happy years.

Richard, with a father-in-law who provided every comfort for his family, did not need to enlarge his law practice and so spent more and more time pursuing political interests. Although George was not actively involved in politics, he had strong opinions and unobtrusively his influence was often exercised. He often helped his son-in-law in his political aspirations and he was ever ready to give to causes which interested him.

In 1881, the same year George built Devon House, an incident occurred which would have an impact on Jamaica. The governor becoming suspicious of the purposes of a ship, the *Florence*, on its way from Venezuela, ordered her to be detained. A case was brought against the governor and his agent, and the *Florence* was awarded damages amounting to £6000. The British government ordered the local Legislative Council to vote the money, but the council objected strenuously, arguing that the governor had acted not in local interests but in imperial interests. This incident led to strong agitation against the Crown Colony government and Richard was in the forefront of the fight.

In 1883 Richard made a trip to England and joined a deputation from Jamaica to wait on the Secretary of State for the Colonies. They asked that control over the expenditure of the island's revenue to be given to the non-official members of the Legislative Council. This request was favourably received by the British government, and when Sir Henry Norman arrived later the same year as the new governor, succeeding Sir Anthony Musgrave, he brought with him the order which gave Jamaica a new form of government, which consisted of the 'Governor and nine nominated and nine elected members.' Whatever say this gave the elected part of the government in the running of affairs could however be vetoed by the governor with his controlling vote. But in this new legislature the elected members were given financial control over government expenditure.

It would have been a merry night at Devon House when the news arrived. George and Richard would have considered such an occasion worthy of a party. But not so Charles Hamilton Jackson, Richard's uncle who had voted to make Jamaica a Crown Colony after the Morant Bay Rebellion. He was incensed at his nephew and wrote a letter to George Stiebel stating, 'I would like to call on you but as long as that rascal Jackson is living in your house, I shall not do so.' Uncle Charles became known in the family as 'Traitor Jackson' while Richard earned the name 'Patriot Jackson'.

In 1882 when there had been an attempted assassination of Queen Victoria, George attended a meeting held by the Custos of Kingston at the town hall to consider suggestions to celebrate the Queen's escape. *Hands all round*, a poem by Lord Tennyson was discussed, and the idea was that the colonies all round the world should sing the song on the same day as a sign of affection and loyalty to the Queen.

It was in Sir Henry Norman's time that George was asked to be Custos of St Andrew. This was indeed an honour for him as this position had traditionally been given to members of the plantocracy and gentry. The governor had accepted this self-made man at King's House, and society would follow the Queen's representative. Frequently the governor rode down from King's House and had breakfast with George on the west balcony.

Now George was expected to do more entertaining than ever before. Garden parties were held on the lawns of Devon House and Magdalen and Theresa had to host the many large dinner parties where the courses were seemingly endless. The best English china was used, silver glistened and crystal shimmered in the gas and candle light. On their trips to Europe, George, who was an inveterate collector, bought so much silver, china and figurines that he had filled the shelves in the fire-proof vault on the west of the house.

All this entertaining required a large staff. There were three or four gardeners, two house maids, a butler, a cook, a laundress, grooms and a coachman at Devon House and they too were entertained royally especially at Christmas; an ox was roasted in the garden and the staff were also served turkey and ham with all the trimmings. The Stiebel Jacksons had a reputation for being very kind to their staff and a coachman from King's House even left his employment there to work with George, as the coachman also thought George's horses were the finest in the town.

Many years later we find in the St Andrew Parish Church a touching inscription on a tombstone: 'In memory of Amelia Francis the faithful and greatly beloved servant of Mrs Richard Hill Jackson who died March 9th 1911.'

Custos George lived a busy life as he was invited to all parish functions and all official parties. On 13 April 1887, the Governor, Sir Henry Norman, addressed his Legislative Council about a permanent commemoration of Queen Victoria's Jubilee saying, 'As yet not much had been subscribed or promised to the proposed Hospital.' This is today's Jubilee Hospital, built for the purpose of training nurses to attend women in childbirth. The Governor went on, 'I take this opportunity of acknowledging with gratitude the munificence for this object of...£100 from Mr George Stiebel.'

The next governor, Sir Henry Blake, organized the Jamaica Exhibition of 1891. Five hotels were built to accommodate the visitors and over three hundred thousand people visited the exhibition. Sir Henry thought the exhibition would be a good way of advertising the island, but even then Jamaica was short of funds so George loaned the government £5000 to carry on the work and gave a guarantee of a further £1000. The exhibition was opened by Prince George who later became King George V. In recognition of his unselfish services in the interests of the island, the old Queen in her May honours bestowed the CMG on George. Later he went to England to receive the medal from Queen Victoria. The boy of 14 who ran away from school had come a long way.

Richard Jackson too was very prominent in public life as he was Mayor of Kingston in 1889 and 1890. He also owned two properties, one of about 1100 acres which encompassed what is now Washington Boulevard, and another property in St Thomas, Albion Mountain. It is today in the hands of the Administrator-General as today's heir, Richard Jackson, grandson of Richard Hill Jackson, refuses to accept the estate as in the 1970s squatters invaded the property and 'captured' it. Added to this complication there is an enormous tax bill owing. After Richard Hill Jackson's death, the Kingston property was sold for £1100 and went towards paying his debts.

Richard was very popular with the electorate and many years after his death in 1944, a deputation of elderly Kingston citizens went to his last born and only surviving son, Arthur Jackson, and asked him if he would stand for election. Arthur firmly refused, explaining that because of politics his father had died a pauper. One old man replied with feeling, 'Ah, Massa Arthur, that was because your father was an honest man!'

Many of us owe Richard Jackson a great debt of gratitude. When the Wolmer's Trust was in difficulties during the time that he was mayor he arranged for the KSAC to buy the Wolmer's schoolyard which was then situated next to the Kingston Parish Church. The mayor, after selling the schoolyard, arranged for the purchase of the present Wolmer's site which is to be seen today on the north side of National Heroes Circle.

One of his acts as mayor which endeared him to the hearts of Jamaicans was the day that he locked out the governor and a visiting dignitary from the town hall because they had decided to change the time of the welcoming ceremony. Richard Hill Jackson, a rebel at heart, as are most Jamaicans, considered this a slight to the citizens of Kingston. The people were delighted at their mayor's actions and 'wags made up a ditty which was sung to celebrate the occasion.'

The year after the exhibition Magdalen became ill. Little is known of this good wife and mother, so conscientious in saving all the money that her husband had sent to be spent on herself, but one thing we do know from the will that George made in 1890, was that he had done his best to ensure her comfort after his death. 'To my beloved wife Magdalen Stiebel an annuity of £1000 . . . .' He also left her Devon House and all its contents, even mentioning the fences and specifying that it all be kept in a state of good repair at the expense of the estate. He left her his carriage and her selection of his buggies. She was also to have use of the market cart and he left her his best pair of horses complete with harness and she was to choose the mule she wanted for the cart. He ordered that if a horse or mule should die or become unfit for work it should be replaced at the request of his wife and the expense of his estate. But these provisions never came into force as she died before he did.

From George's will we know that Magdalen's sister, Sarah Jane, was living with them at Devon House. Often spinsters in the family lived with their married brothers or sisters. The generous man to whom the Baker family had objected, was to hold no grudge; he also left an annuity to his sister-in-law Sarah Jane of £100 for her lifetime.

The first great tragedy was to strike at Devon House on 12 October 1892 when Magdalen died. An announcement appeared in the press: 'Yesterday at Devon House St Andrew, Magdalen the beloved wife of the Hon George Stiebel died. The funeral will move at 5 o'clock this afternoon for the Half Way Tree cemetery. Friends and acquaintances will please accept this intimation.'

Under a grey granite tombstone with a white marble cross wreathed in white marble flowers, Magdalen was laid to rest. The inscription reads, 'In memory of Magdalen wife of George Stiebel CMG Custos of St Andrew who died on the 12 day of October 1892 aged 67 years.' George had imported enough grey granite from Scotland to bury the whole family.

George sadly returned to his beautiful home having lost the woman that he had loved so faithfully from his youth. But life went on and he had little time for sorrow with six grandchildren around him.

An eagerly anticipated event by the family at Devon House was the summer holidays, when the whole family packed up to go and spend the hot months in the cool of Brown's Town. Then there was all bustle with staff running up and down stairs with trunks and the grooms packing the buggies. It was a long drive to Minard, and the children's excitement grew as they neared the lovely old house, which had been built in the days of slavery. Here the boys climbed the stone walls and the girls went to the cow pen in the mornings to watch the cows being milked. George's first task was to see that the

Union Jack was hoisted so that the neighbours who lived on distant hills would know that the family was in residence and would come calling.

There were walks across the pastures to the woodlands on top of the hills and there they sometimes picnicked. They went to the sea for picnics too and they had the thrill of going down the beautiful Fern Gully gorge where ferns clustered close to the narrow marl road and trees kept out the sunlight overhead. It was a dangerous drive in those days and as the horses could not stop easily if there was an oncoming carriage, out-riders went ahead sounding bugles to give warning of the descending carriage.

Richard, the children's father, was now a middle-aged man and from a photograph of him we can see that his hearty appetite had made him a portly gentleman. He looked like Edward VII and resembled him in more ways than one; like the King, women still found Richard very attractive and this caused some difficulties in

Edward VII lookalike Richard Hill Jackson. He loved food and women loved him.

the family. It may have been because of this that Theresa decided to take the children to school in England. Her father was in full agreement and it was he who paid for their education. It was 1894 when they decided to go. George, the eldest son, was 14 years old and the baby, Arthur, was 3. Richard was reluctant to see all his family go and insisted that at least one child must be left to keep his company so his favourite son Douglas, who was 10 years old, was told to remain with his father at Devon House.

Cabin trunks which stood 4 feet high were packed and the Hon George organized everything for his daughter and accompanied her to England. He insisted on carrying a cow on board so that his 3-year-old grandson Arthur would have fresh milk on the long voyage. A nanny also went along to look after this youngest child. They went straight to their house in Wimpole Street, which was fully equipped to receive them with staff, and complete with carriage and coachman. Theresa had often gone to England on holidays with her parents and stayed at this house. When they were settled Magdalen Hilda, who was called Maggie by the family and who was the first child born at Devon House, and Gladys and Amy were sent to Miss Geich's school for girls, which was one of the best girls' schools in England at that time. George was sent to a boys' public school, and as soon as baby Arthur was old enough he was sent to St Paul's Preparatory School. When Theresa and the children were well settled, George returned to Jamaica.

A year later tragedy again struck Devon House. Richard and Theresa's promising son Douglas, now 11, developed and quickly succumbed to typhoid. There was no chance of the family in England being able to attend the funeral. The bereaved father was alone in his sorrow, except for the comfort of his father-in-law.

Richard and George followed the small coffin to its final resting place beside the boy's grandmother in the Half Way Tree Parish Church-yard. His tomb was entirely of white marble, and the inscription reads, 'Blessed are the pure in heart for they shall see God. Sacred to the memory of Douglas Hill Stiebel. The beloved child of Richard and Theresa Jackson who entered into rest 7th June 1895 aged 11. For he doth not afflict willingly nor grieve the children of men.'

No more than a week after the death of the golden-haired son we find Richard taking his customary swim after a hot day's work in Kingston in the swimming pool at Devon House. Family tradition recounts that his butler had just brought him a cup of tea which he had balanced on his stomach, when he had a heart attack, but *Gall's News Letter* give us another version:

> Mayor of Kingston Mr Jackson had a severe attack of influenza which did not cause any anxiety as he was young and of strong and healthy constitution, but the disease developed into acute bronchitis and he grew gradually worse until pneumonia set in and he breathed his last at two o'clock in the morning.

It could be that Richard had had a heart attack in the swimming pool and then developed pneumonia. *Galls News Letter* goes on to describe the preparations for the funeral:

> On the news of the Mayor's death becoming known in town, orders were issued by the Deputy Chairman of the City Council Mr S. Watson for the convention of an informal meeting of the members at 10 a.m. Shortly after that hour Messrs Watson, Banton, Brandon, Ffrench and Burke assembled in the council room together with a number of other citizens. Mr Watson who occupied the chair intimated that the meeting had been called for the purpose of deciding what arrangements should be made by the council for taking part in the funeral of the Mayor. He suggested that he be authorised to proceed to Devon Penn and see Mr Stiebel with the view of getting the latter's consent to have the body moved to Kingston and the service held in the Parish Church so that the people of Kingston might have the opportunity of paying their respects to the dead Mayor. Mr Watson also suggested that the city council as a body should leave the Town Hall at 4 p.m. and proceed to Devon Penn for which carriages would be ordered and the employees of the Council would also be directed to attend. Mr

Ffrench suggested that all the arrangements be left in the hands of the Vice Chairman which he agreed to. Mr R. H. Waites then asked permission to address the board, which having been granted he proceeded to say that there was a general consensus that something more than had been suggested by Mr Watson should be done. He (the speaker) had walked along the streets and had heard a strong expression of opinion that Mr Jackson should be given a public funeral...Mr Jackson had rendered yeoman service to Kingston especially and the citizens were desirous of rendering all the honours possible to their deceased countryman.... Mr Watson said that he knew that Mr Stiebel was a man who did not care for ostentation and perhaps he would object to the body lying in state and he, Mr Watson, would urge Mr Stiebel to acquiesce in the wishes of the people.

The City Surveyor was then directed to drape the City Hall in black on the understanding that Mr Watson would make all arrangements. The meeting adjourned. At about 12 o'clock it became known that as Mr Stiebel had no objections, the Mayor was to be accorded a public funeral and the body was to lie in state at the Town Hall. Placards were posted calling upon the citizens of Kingston to assemble at the Town Hall at 4 o'clock and accompany the body to the Parish Church where a service was to be held. It was arranged that the members of the City Council should leave at 3 p.m. for Devon Penn, to accompany the body to the City Hall. Meanwhile, the latter building had been heavily draped in black both inside and out and a catafalque had been erected on which to rest the coffin. It was placed in the centre of the room and it stood three feet six inches high. It was covered with sable velvet and cotton cloth and was arranged with funeral wreaths. Towards 4 o'clock the vicinity of the Town Hall became packed with a crowd...large details of mounted constabulary kept the streets and the approaches of the Town Hall clear and precisely at five minutes to 5 o'clock the body, accompanied by the City Councillors, appeared in view on Duke Street. A few minutes later the procession arrived in front of the Town Hall at which time the band of the Kingston Infantry Militia played the dead march in Saul and the coffin was taken from the hearse, up the stairs and deposited on the catalfalque .... Then ensued a scene of indescribable confusion. The Town Hall now became filled and there was a terrific rush to obtain a view of the deceased. No provision whatever had been made to secure an orderly procession, and this portion of the proceedings was certainly devoid of anything like order or decency. The services of the constabulary were evidently enlisted, and the crowd kept off. After remaining in the Town Hall for about half an hour the body was again placed in the hearse and the cortege proceeded to the Parish Church in the following order: The Kingston Volunteer Militia Band; An escort of Police; Mounted Police; The body; Mounted Police; The Pall Bearers; His Excellency, the Governor and Staff; Members of Her Majesty's Privy Council; Members of the Legislative Council; The Vice Chairman of the City Council; Members of Council of Kingston; the Custos of St Andrew; Magistrates of Kingston and St Andrew; The Chairman of the Parochial Board of St Catherine; The Judges of the Supreme Court; The Resident Magistrates; Barristers, Advocates and Solicitors; Officers of the Army and Navy; and Friends and acquaintances of the deceased and the general public. On arrival at the Church the body was met at the entrance by his Lordship the Bishop, Enos Nuttall, who was a close friend of the family.

Galls News Letter tells us:

The painful part of it is that Mrs Jackson who herself is in poor health is in England and not yet fully informed of the death of her son Master Douglas Jackson at Devon House from typhoid fever a few weeks ago just prior to his father becoming afflicted with influenza. The severity of such a sudden double bereavement would be hard to bear under ordinary circumstances but let us hope 'He that doth the Raven feed and providently caters for His sparrow' may soothe and comfort the widow in this hour of her deep distress. It is for her we must all feel most ... a loving mother and devoted wife, five thousand miles away from those who summed up the total of all that she loved and cared for in this world.

The loss of Mr Jackson at a time like this is one that is not to be easily measured, either by the city that he represented as Mayor or the Parish he so ably represented as legislator. The legal profession has lost an able and experienced member and his many warm friends, a most intelligent and entertaining companion. He had done much for Kingston which can ill spare him at present. He was the idol of the people of St Catherine and the terror of all evil doers who stood and trembled at his name and the chances of his getting on the scent of their covert designs.

It appears that from the Parish Church in Kingston his body was carried back to Devon House having had much buffeting to and fro before being finally laid to rest. The *News Letter* goes on:

> His mortal remains were conveyed yesterday afternoon from Devon House to their last resting place in the churchyard of Half Way Tree followed by an immense procession of friends in carriages.
>
> There was gloom cast over the whole district and the roads were lined on either side by a respectful crowd who made every possible demonstration of grief and sympathy with the family of the Custos of Kingston.... Suffice it to say that both in England and in this country Mr Jackson has omitted no opportunity of either protecting the rights of the people or serving the best interests of the island. To sum it up it can be fairly said that in the brief 26 years during which Mr Jackson has been before the public he has lived an eventful and useful life making a name, which those he leaves behind to mourn his loss may be justly proud.

Richard Jackson was buried beside his son under a grey granite tombstone on which rested a plain white marble cross. Inscribed on the tomb was, 'Sacred to the memory of Richard Hill Jackson born April 24th 1846 died June 26th 1895. Ego tamen non obliciscartut,' which means 'Nevertheless, I shall not forget you.'

George seemed to have lost heart. He suffered from Bright's disease and for some time after was unable to leave his home. When at last he did recover and go out, the *Jamaica Post* reports that 'people were surprised to see the change that was wrought in him.' He lived for another year and in June 1896 Dr Saunders, his doctor, ordered him to transact no more business. He gradually grew worse, and it is sad to think of this wonderful man who was so

An ageing George Stiebel. He died in 1896 with no close family member beside him.

devoted to his family having no close member near him in his last days. But of course Theresa could not leave five young children in London and even with steamships, she could not get to Jamaica under weeks.

The *Daily Gleaner* reported on 30 June 1896, 'We regret to announce the death of Hon George Stiebel CMG which occurred at his home Devon House St Andrew yesterday afternoon. For some months the deceased gentleman had displayed signs of failing health.... On Sunday his illness took a serious turn and the sad news that he was dying was current in the city yesterday morning.' It went on to give a résumé of his life and one of the tributes paid him was that 'In private life he was known to be kind-hearted and liberal and he has given a helping hand to many standing in need of monetary assistance.'

His death was widely regretted, as evidenced by a quote from a resolution of the Parochial Board of St Andrew, dated 7 July 1896 and sent to his daughter, Mrs R. H. Jackson: 'With profound regret we record the death, since our last meeting, of our beloved chairman the Hon George Stiebel CMG.' From 1884 when he was unanimously elected chairman he had occupied the position until his death. The *Jamaica Post* recorded in an obituary, 'Mr Stiebel was very kind to the poor and many a household will shed tears of regret and sorrow at hearing of his loss.' Another newspaper report of him records that in spite of his princely fortune, he...

> always remained a man of unpretending deportment and the most unobtrusive habits, he has never forsaken or forgotten his old friends... on the contrary his sympathies have always been with the poor who are so often forgotten in this world.... Mr Stiebel has done very many acts of secret kindness which the world will never know... the wealth God had blessed him with and the influence his own force of character has secured for him with every class, have all tended to awake in his own soul the earnest desire to make all this conserve to the public usefulness, the amelioration of suffering and distress and to help the struggling.... There is no more noble character living than George Stiebel.

All the newspapers paid tribute to the Hon George. *Gall's News Letter* of 30 June tells us that...

> after a severe illness which he bore with characteristic resignation and courage, the death of his beloved wife not very long ago was a heavy blow, which had a depressing effect on his health and spirits from which he was unable to completely recover. Mr Stiebel by fortunate investment in South American mines amassed a large fortune which never spoiled the sweet simplicity of a gentle, amiable disposition and which he used not only to help cases of deserving individual's distress but to assist agencies and institutions having for their object the industrial, education and the religious advancement of the people.... Mr Stiebel was beloved as well as esteemed for his amiable personal qualities and for his upright character.

The *Gleaner* of 1 July reported the funeral:

> The last and most melancholy act following upon the lamented death of Hon George Stiebel was consummated yesterday afternoon

in the presence of a large gathering of the deceased's sorrowing relatives and acquaintances. The funeral cortege started from Devon House... proceeded to the Parish Church of St Andrew at Half Way Tree. At the Church the Rev Mr Isaacs conducted the services with all the impressiveness and solemnity attending the Anglican rites. The metallic coffin encasing the remains of the late Mr Stiebel rested on the bier in the nave of the church and was covered with a profusion of wreaths from those who respected his memory.... It had been decided that the St Andrew Parochial Board should in its corporate capacity attest to the feeling which animated the members in regard for the deceased Chairman by attending in one body but owing to the suddenness of the call and the short period elapsing between the death and the burial the intention of the members had to be abandoned. But the members of the Board individually were present in large numbers; the funeral although large was unostentatious and mainly without pomp.

Interior of St. Andrew Parish Church.

The custos was buried beside his wife under the Scottish grey granite which, not having weathered at all, still shines today. The inscription reads, 'In loving memory of George Stiebel CMG who died 29 June 1896 aged 75. Thy faith hath made thee whole.' A large white marble cross lies across the granite.

George had provided generously for his daughter and grandchildren. In his will he requested that each of his grandchildren when they were 10 years old be sent to a school 'of good character and standing', in Great Britain or Europe. He went on to say that the boys should stay at school until they were ready to go to university and the girls should stay at school for at least five years, as he wanted all his grandchildren to have a first-class education, but he cautioned his trustees to see that it was also a liberal schooling. He requested that the trust pay clothing and maintenance of each grandchild during the holidays, but not exceeding £300 per annum for each child. While at university each grandson was to be allowed £400 per annum and if any of his granddaughters wanted to study a profession they were to be allowed the same income. When the boys had completed their university course they were to be allowed £300 per annum until they came of age and their grandfather deemed them of age, when the boys were 25 and the girls 21. At this age each grandson should inherit £10 000 and a further £10 000 should be put in trust when each granddaughter was of age for her lifetime, and this was to go to any children that she might have, for their education and maintenance. He even mentioned that each child should be given £50 for their return passage money and travelling expenses to Jamaica when they had finished their education.

He also left his daughter an annuity of £3000. He directed that Devon House was not to be sold in the lifetime of his daughter 'unless she consents to do so in her own handwriting and I declare that if she should wish to do so she shall have the right to sell.... I direct that until Devon House is sold it be kept in good repair at the expense of my estate.' He directed that a person be appointed to keep the accounts of the estate at a sum not exceeding £300 per annum. He advised his trustees to invest in government savings. In case the lawyer who was handling his affairs predeceased him, he appointed another, Ernest Nuttall, and failing him, Arthur Farquharson. He requested that 'Messrs Stiebel Brothers of 8 Crosby Square, London should be requested to act in the matter of my estate in England.'

After his wife's death he had bequeathed a pair of silver candlesticks to each of his three granddaughters. And to his grandson George, 'and in case of his death to his eldest surviving brother and if none to his surviving sister, my chiming clock called Westminster. A specific present from me to my granddaughter Magdalen Hilda or in the case of her death her surviving sister, my drawing room onyx clock.' He even provided for the payment for monuments to his wife and himself. The will continued:

> I give and divest to my said daughter during her lifetime the use of the dwelling house at Minard together with the out-buildings, appendages, furniture and other goods and chattels for the use of persons occupying the said home and together with a full supply of milk from the breeding stock on Minard whenever she resides there and the right to pasture horses not exceeding six in number.

The annuity that he left Theresa of £3000 was free of all duties. He also left her an account in the National Provincial Bank of England. Besides leaving sums of money to numerous godchildren he left £200 to be invested and the interest given to the Ebenezer Chapel in Kingston for the benefit of the Dorcas Society. 'I give to my coachman David McCulloch the sum of 4 shillings to be paid to him weekly as long as he shall live.' In those days meat was 3 penny a pound.

The contents of the iron safe at Devon House 'belong to and are the absolute property of Theresa.... I desire that if his college course is not complete at my death that George...be kept at Cambridge at the expense of my estate for two years at the rate of

£220 for each year and that at the conclusion of his curriculum ... if he wished to return to Jamaica, his passage will be paid as a second class passenger.' It seems extraordinary that after giving George an education at Cambridge, his grandfather should want him to return as a second-class passenger. Doubtless he thought that the young should not be extravagant and should learn to 'rough it'. He directed his trustees to 'inspect and examine the lands on which I hold mortgages to see that they are kept in proper order,' and that if they should find it difficult to collect the interest they 'ought to at once realize.' The securities held for me by the National Provincial Bank of England are not to be sold or disposed of except after the consultation with Messrs Stiebel Bros., for I bought them on their recommendation and having confidence in them would not sell without their recommendation.'

Someone was to be employed to prepare a balance sheet with the funds of his estate; 'every month a copy should be sent to my daughter either in Jamaica or if she is living abroad within ten days.... I direct to my trustees to pay to the treasurer of the Parish Church at Half Way Tree the sum of £20 annually for pew rent for that church unless my daughter directs that it be discontinued.' He said that no trust money was to be invested in land unless the title was produced. He continued to leave instructions: 'Invest the residuary fund in any of the public stock funds or government securities of the U.K. of Great Britain or of India or of this island or of any other colony or dependency of Great Britain and upon freehold securities in Great Britain or buy any debentures guaranteed by the Government Savings Bank of this island. As to my shares in the Callas Gold Mining Company I direct that they should be sent to Messrs Stiebel Bros. of 8 Crosby Square, London to be sold as soon after my decease as the Stiebel Bros. deem it advantageous.' He said that all his properties were to be sold with 'the exception of Lloyd and the machinery fixtures live and dead stock and my Penn called Salt Pond to be sold as soon as practicable. The sugar estates to be sold with or without engines, machines, fixtures, waines, waggons, tool implements, utensils, cattle, mules, horse kind or live or dead stock. They must be sold within ten years.' He was so meticulous about every detail, and yet for all his care, the estate evidently was not well handled and the heirs were constantly bickering with the trustees.

CHAPTER 3
The Stiebel Jacksons

The part that Theresa Stiebel Jackson had played as hostess in Devon House to the Custos and Mayor of Kingston had left its mark on her, and in a crayon portrait, which her daughter-in-law has at Abbey Court, we see a very dignified and commanding woman. It was drawn while she lived in England and she has a fur draped across her shoulder. Theresa was 40 at the time of her father's death. After having a father who attended to every detail of her life, she found it very hard to deal with trustees, and to mother and father her five children. It was however the elegant Edwardian days when living in England was very comfortable, and Theresa had enough money to live in the style to which she had been accustomed. She also had her Stiebel relations to advise her on problems.

Her father had lived to see his grandson George at Cambridge. He was a charming boy from all reports, and at 16 was a help to his mother. He was very athletic, played a good game of tennis, rowed for Cambridge and later became a Cambridge blue. The girls played the piano and sang, it was said to concert standards. At St Paul's, Arthur learnt to box and there he met a fellow pupil who in the Second World War rose to the rank of Field Marshal and became the famous Viscount Montgomery of Alamein.

They lived in England while they were being educated and often Theresa took them for holidays on the continent. They

A crayon portrait of Theresa Stiebel Jackson.

travelled with their own coach, English coachman and personal maids. On one occasion they were on their way to Switzerland when the coach broke down and a count who was passing by offered his help. In the course of the conversation he discovered that he had met Mrs Jackson's father some years before in France, and he invited her and her family to visit his nearby castle while repairs were being done to their coach. The count was fascinated by Theresa and asked her to marry him, but she refused the proposal considering herself at 40 too old for remarriage.

After George graduated from Cambridge he studied law. He was called to the Bar in England, but with money left by his grandfather he lived well and there was little incentive to work. He had his mother and three sisters to escort to parties and functions. In 1901 Queen Victoria died and Edward VII ascended the throne. These were the gay Edwardian days and the Stiebel Jacksons were 'in society'. The girls were attractive teenagers and Theresa always saw that they were dressed in French models. When they went riding in their carriage in Hyde Park which was fashionable for high society, Edward VII would raise his hat to them.

In 1903 Theresa bought herself a Rolls Royce. Arthur was delighted as he had learnt to drive although he was only 12. Cars were few and far between, and the driving licence had not yet been introduced. His mother decided that he was such a good driver that he should drive herself and the girls around Europe. In spite of all the thrill of being 12 years old and driving a Rolls, Arthur complained bitterly at being dragged into every church and cathedral all over the continent. He did however acquire a taste for expensive cars, and all through his life he took a keen interest in automobiles.

George Stiebel would have turned in his grave if he had known that his executors Leopold Schloss, Bishop Nutall and Mr Wood were managing his trust funds badly. The heirs seemed to live in a state of great affluence at one moment or in a state of anxiety as to when their next allowance would arrive. This contention between the heirs and executors continued and the situation became so bad at one time that the matter was taken to court in Jamaica and young George appeared on behalf of himself and the other heirs. It is said that this was his first and last appearance in court!

When the girls had completed their education Mrs Jackson planned to take them back to Devon House, but there was again tragedy in store for her. Maggie, her eldest daughter, after finishing her education developed melancholia. At that time little was known about psychology and there was not much treatment available so, sorrowfully, her mother had to leave her behind in England. They found a family coincidentally with the name of Jackson who agreed to have her and she had permanent nurses and a doctor in attendance.

There was talk of Arthur going to Cambridge but Mrs Jackson decided that there was not enough money to send him there, so he was sent to the Cornwall School of Mines where he became a mining engineer. George was known for being most charming, but it was Arthur who was the character of the family. Having spent his early years in one of the wealthiest families in Jamaica and yet often hearing that there was a shortage of money, he spent his life trying to live like a Shylock at one moment and the next enjoying a grand spending spree. In 1912 when Arthur was 21 his mother was told by her doctor that she had a weak heart and that she would not live six months, so she requested that Arthur join the family at Devon House.

Although there had been severe damage to several buildings in St Andrew in the 1907 earthquate, Devon House had not suffered and looked as splendid as ever when the Jackson family returned to live there. With the young people back at Devon House they immediately entered into the social life of St Andrew, which in those days was hectic. Friends on horseback rode in with invitations to garden parties, picnics and balls. Often a group of them rode on the tram car in their evening dresses to attend dances at the Constant Spring Hotel. At this time the Hope Gardens tram car passed the gates of Devon House, and from Half Way Tree one went to Constant Spring and amongst all classes it was a popular means of transport.

George held many tennis parties at Devon House on the east side where his grandfather's tennis courts were still well kept. Sometimes Gladys and Amy would join in foursomes and in their long skirts they would glide across the courts, gently chasing the balls. The girls often arranged musical evenings with the Taylors who frequently visited their uncle at 'Reka Dom'. Arthur had invested in a racehorse and his greatest delight was to train the horse on his grandfather's racecourse at Devon House.

In 1914 the First World War broke out and Arthur joined the British West India Regiment. When he had completed his training at Up Park Camp he passed out as a lieutenant and sailed with the second contingent which left for England early in 1916. On his arrival he went immediately to Hawks of Saville Row and was fitted out with uniforms. While serving he was chosen as heavyweight

A dashing Arthur Jackson in uniform. He loved horse-racing, new cars and telling funny stories.

champion of the allied forces in Italy. All through his life he was to take a keen interest in boxing. His war stories were many, and in true Stiebel style, when he was on leave he rented an entire hotel for the use of himself and his friends.

But at Devon House tragedy had struck again. Gladys had become psychologically disturbed and had to be put in hospital. The family saw to it that she had a bungalow to herself and private nurses round the clock. Meals were sent to her from Myrtle Bank Hotel by taxi and her own grand piano was installed so that when she had visitors she could sing and play for them. Her mother was so distressed that she could hardly bear to visit her. Unfortunately, there was little to be done for her as there were then few treatments for these problems.

In the meantime her sister Amy had become bored with the round of parties and volunteered to teach music at St Hilda's School for Girls in Brown's Town.

Theresa, who was now living alone with George at Devon House, was putting on more and more weight which was not good for her heart condition. She had great difficulty in going up and down stairs, so George installed a lift at Devon House, the first in Jamaica. It was not an electric one, so one of the male staff had to pull up the lift and let it down. His mother still occupied the master bedroom and George used the large room on the west side of the house.

They were now living quietly at Devon House and with three of the four children away and so much sadness in the family, there was little heart for entertainment. But they still had a large staff including a cook, a butler, two housemaids, a laundress, three or four gardeners, grooms and a coachman who also was the chauffeur. They owned a single and a double buggy and also had two cars.

When the First World War ended the Jamaican soldiers in the British West India Regiment returned to a resounding welcome in Kingston. Amongst those returning was Arthur who returned to live at Devon House. Although he brought back a sense of fun, Devon House never did regain its former splendour. There was little entertaining, as Mrs Jackson's health declined steadily and by now George was crippled with arthritis. When he discovered that his condition improved in Brown's Town, he bought a house in this inland town and often went to stay there.

Meanwhile, the Jackson family frequently spent a month or so in the summer at a house in Mandeville. It was on such a visit that they met Nora May McDermot. Nora was born in Kingston in 1900, of Irish and French descent.

Arthur McDermot, Nora's father, was a customs officer in Kingston. He married an English girl, Bertha Paine, whose family had long owned property at Hardwar Gap. They had a large family

Nora Jackson. She and her husband Arthur were the last Stiebel Jacksons to live at Devon House.

of seven, Nora was the second of the five girls. Although the family never had much money, with the help of relatives, Nora was sent to Miss Thomas's Boarding School for Girls in Montpelier, St James. When she was only 13 her mother died and she was sent to live in Mandeville with her mother's sister, Mrs Wood, who had married a Scottish accountant. Not long after her mother had died her father decided to leave Jamaica and settle in New York, so Nora was deprived of both parents.

When she met the Jacksons, she was very much taken with the whole family, and they with her. Shortly after this George realized that his mother's health was deteriorating and that without her daughters around, life was lonely for her at Devon House, so he suggested that Mrs Jackson employ Nora as a companion. His mother liked the young girl and was agreeable to the suggestion.

Even today when Nora describes her first visit to Devon House her eyes light up at the memory of the wonder of it all. 'I thought,' she said, 'that it was an Aladdin's Palace. I was so dazzled with its beauty.' All the treasures that George Stiebel had 'picked up' on the continent were a source of joy to the unspoilt girl. She was impressed with Mrs Jackson's charm and they both became fond of each other. A romance blossomed between Arthur and Nora and they agreed to get married but before they could do so, Mrs Jackson died. George and Arthur lived at Devon House during their mother's last illness and Nora watched over her with deep concern as she already looked upon Mrs Jackson as her future mother-in-law.

One of the last things that Mrs Jackson did before her death was to give an organ to the Half Way Tree Parish Church in memory of her father. She died on 23 August 1922, having outlived her husband by twenty-seven years.

She was interred under the grey granite stone from Scotland. On her tombstone was inscribed, 'In loving memory of Theresa Jackson widow of R. H. Jackson who died on 23 August 1922 aged 66. I will give you rest.' With the passing of Mrs Jackson, Devon House seemed to lose its anchorage. All of George Stiebel's money divided between five heirs, meant that no single heir had the means to maintain the large property and it was decided to sell.

A couple of months after Mrs Jackson's death Arthur and Nora were married quietly at Devon House.

Both Arthur and Nora enjoyed living at Devon House. Arthur, like his grandfather George Stiebel, was very keen on horse racing. From the time that he returned to Jamaica he bought and trained horses at Devon House on his grandfather's racetrack. One of his most famous horses was Rumpelstiltskin which won the Jamaican Derby, the Lonsdale Cup, the Caribbean Cup twice and most of the big cup races. A friend who used to go with him to the races sometimes shared a ticket with him. On one occasion the ticket was four shillings. 'Let's buy a £1 ticket,' suggested his friend but

Arthur replied, 'Goodness, no man, that's too expensive.' Arthur seldom placed a bet at a race meeting and never on his own horse, as he feared this might make his horse lose.

In addition to horses he had a childish joy in buying new cars. Shortly after they were married Nora was standing on the front balcony at Devon House, when she saw a large car driving at tremendous speed up Hope Road. To her surprise the long car turned into the gate of Devon House and Arthur got out and invited her to go for a drive in his new Italian Bugatti.

He was always impressing on Nora that he was a very poor man, and from time to time he was haunted by the thought that he might lose all his money. At such times he went on one of his stringent economizing programmes. His idea of economy was to buy in quantity in order to get a discount. Once he came home with a quarter dozen watches bought at the Swiss Stores. Another day when he was bent on living frugally he brought home a dozen pairs of shoes all the same size. When Nora asked him to buy some combs, he arrived with a gross!

Arthur was a great character and well loved wherever he went. There are many stories in the family about him. The young bride never failed to be fascinated with the tales which he related as they sat on an evening in the lovely old Devon House. At 90, she still remembers some of these stories. Although Arthur was not a habitual heavy drinker, he enjoyed a night out drinking with his male friends. One night he and a friend spent the night out in Sav-la-mar. They lost track of time, and on emerging from the bar, they hailed a passer-by and asked him whether it was the sun or moon shining. The stranger took a good look at them and replied, 'I don't know, gentlemen. I am a stranger in these parts.'

Years later Nora gave her husband an ocean going yacht which was christened 'Nora May'. When the 1951 hurricane threatened Jamaica, the yacht was too large to enter the anchorage at Port Royal and was anchored at Harbour Head. Arthur left the Caymanian boatman on board well stocked with beef steaks for the eventful night. The day after the hurricane, all they could see of the Nora May was the tip of her mast sticking out of the water. 'Poor fellow,' said the owner, 'he must have gone down with the boat. I hope he enjoyed the steaks before his death.'

Arthur drove sadly home lamenting that he had forgotten to insure the yacht. As they turned into the Lady Musgrave Road driveway who should appear, but the Caymanian boatman. 'You damn rascal,' roared Arthur, 'why didn't you stay with your ship and where are the steaks?' The boatman grinned from ear to ear; he knew 'Squire' too well to be offended. The Arthur Jacksons lost their roof at their home on Lady Musgrave Road but their former home Devon House remained unscathed during the horrendous winds.

Nora and Arthur were the last Stiebel Jacksons to live at Devon House. After Mrs Jackson's death they did not stay long as the house was put up for sale in 1923. It was bought by Reginald Melhado for £5000.

Arthur was not a 'go getter' like his grandfather, the role of 'landed gentry' was to him far more appealing, so he bought a property called White Hall in St Elizabeth and took his wife to live there. As they had little furniture of their own they took as part of their inheritance some of the furniture from Devon House. One day when Nora was in the silver vault she opened a trunk which was stacked full of Dresden and other figurines. 'Oh, Arthur, couldn't I have one or two pieces?' 'No,' her husband refused, 'you can't even have one; it all belongs to the estate.' The vast amount of china, linen, crystal and silver went for a song.

Arthur and Nora did not live long at White Hall, but bought a small property called Russell Place near Kendal in Manchester. It was here that they had their family. The first born was Richard and quick in succession followed Marjorie, Brunhilde, Audrey and Jennifer. The family have happy memories of Russell Place which had 300 acres of land.

In 1927, five years after Mrs Jackson died, Amy married Harry

Jackson in Mandeville. Although his name was Jackson, they were not related. The marriage started happily, but something went wrong and on 8 August 1933 she committed suicide at her home in Mandeville. There is a story that is told that this suicide took place in the attic at Devon House, but this is not the case. Shortly after, Gladys, who had not recovered from her psychological problems, died on 13 November 1933 at the age of 48 and was buried beside her relatives at the St Andrew Parish Church. The inscription on her tombstone is simple; 'Sacred to the memory of Gladys Nesta S. Jackson, born Nov 22, 1885, died November 13, 1933. Rest in Peace.' An organ chamber was erected in the church in memory of the two sisters Amy and Gladys. That year was a sad year for the Jacksons. You will remember that Maggie Jackson had been left in the care of a family in England some thirty years before. She was the last remaining sister and she died in England that same year. Arthur had now lost all his sisters and their share of the Stiebel estate fell back into the trust fund.

Five years later he also lost his only brother George, who had become more and more crippled by arthritis. He was buried at the Half Way Tree Parish Church beside his family. The inscription reads, 'In loving memory of George Stiebel Jackson died May 1, 1938, in his 58th year. Thy will be done.'

As most of the income which Arthur's sisters and brothers had enjoyed fell back into the Stiebel Trust Fund, Arthur now became a very wealthy man. In spite of this he blamed Nora for their extravagant style of living. Arthur one day asked his son-in-law to look through his cheque book to see that his calculations were correct. On the stub of almost every cheque Gordon Miller noticed a large N. When Arthur was asked why this was so, he said that was Nora's share of the expenditure. His son-in-law patiently pointed out that these cheques were for groceries and motor car expenses. Arthur explained impatiently that if he hadn't been married he would not have had any of these expenses as he would have lived in a tent!

Arthur Jackson with daughter Audrey at her wedding.

There is an amusing story about a diamond tiara that George Stiebel had given his daughter Theresa. It was last used as the wedding head-dress of Arthur's daughter Audrey. Later there was a family discussion as to whom this tiara was to be left. It was decided that it was to be left to Richard as he was the son, but he refused to have it as he said he could not afford to insure such a piece of jewellery. As the argument became more heated, Arthur went for his hacksaw and cut the tiara into five parts. 'There,' he said, 'the problem is solved. Now you can all have diamonds.'

In 1961 Arthur had a stroke from which he only partially recovered. He died on 28 April 1968, at the age of 77 and was buried with his family at Half Way Tree. His widow Nora lives today at Abbey Court Apartments facing Devon House. She was the last bride to be married at Devon House while it was privately owned, and her memories of the lovely home are still vivid. And to the end of his days Arthur regretted leaving Devon House as he said, 'After Devon House and all the comfort that went with it, living in any of his other dwellings was like living in a tent.'

CHAPTER 4

Reggie Melhado

When Devon House was put up for sale after Theresa Stiebel Jackson's death it was purchased in 1923 by Reginald Melhado, a successful entrepreneur along with his partner Harold Davies for £5000. Although Reginald no doubt appreciated the beauty of the old house, he obviously bought it for speculation. Approximately 11 acres around the house were kept while the remaining 40 odd acres were subdivided. It was then that roads such as Waterloo Avenue, Devon Road, and the like, appeared on the maps of the parish of St Andrew for the first time. The furniture of Devon House was advertised for sale by public auction on Wednesday, 21 February 1923.

Originally the Melhado family were Sephardic Jews who had been forced to leave Portugal under the Inquisition in the fifteenth century. Family tradition claims that the Melhados were in Jamaica under Spanish rule and that they and their slaves helped the English to drive out the Spaniards in 1655.

Reginald Henriques Melhado was born on 9 January 1863. He was the son of Mr and Mrs Abraham Melhado of Old Harbour where the Melhados had dry goods stores and were produce dealers. They also exported logwood which was in great demand abroad. Reggie spent his early years in Old Harbour and later attended a boarding school in Kingston.

When Reggie had completed his schooling he returned to Old Harbour and went into the family business where he soon proved himself to be a shrewd businessman. In the old town there lived another Jewish family called the Dolphys. Reggie became fond of Irene Dolphy and married her on 11 August 1886, when he was 23 years old.

Their first child was a girl who was given the unusual Egyptian name, Isis. Three boys followed, Reginald, Vernon and Colin who were all born in Old Harbour. By 1888 the family had moved to Kingston and four more sons were born. Reggie always held that Irene and himself had gone on having children until they had seven boys only in the hope that they would have created another Isis.

The Melhados lived in the fashionable area of Kingston Gardens, where most well-to-do Jewish families lived at that time. It was while living here that the 1907 earthquake and fire occurred which destroyed property to the value of £2,000,000. The synagogue on Duke Street was amongst the buildings destroyed and Reggie, always a public-spirited man, became a member of the rebuilding committee.

The years following the earthquake were good ones for real estate and Reggie went into this business; in fact he was one of the first real estate agents in Jamaica. He was also the founder of the Melhado Brothers and Co which was a merchant firm on Princess Street.

Reggie was always interested in education and he was determined that all his children should be educated in England. He used to say that he and Irene had to eat salt fish to accomplish this, but of course this was not so as by then Reggie was a wealthy man. As soon as Isis was old enough she was sent to Cheltenham Ladies College where, being an intelligent girl, she did very well. It was here that she learnt to think of the poor; she was taught that it was her duty to help those in worse circumstances than herself, a lesson she never forgot. Isis was the first person to have parties for the

The beautiful Isis Melhado, only daughter of Reggie and Irene. She died young at 41.

poor children of Kingston, a practice she carried on for all of her short life. She and a friend also started the Child Welfare Centre.

In 1913 she married Lionel DeMercado, a part owner of Lascelles DeMercado. He took his bride to live at Belmont Great House on Belmont Road. At this time the movement of residences from Kingston to St Andrew had started and Reggie and Irene had moved to 'Fairway' on Oxford Road, close by the newly-wed couple.

A year after Isis's marriage she had a daughter, Dorothy. Reggie and Irene were to see a greal deal of their granddaughter as, living so near, her nanny was able to take Dorothy for walks to visit them. It was not until 1920, six years later, that Paul, Isis's only son was born.

Irene was very close to her daughter and as the years went by she depended on Isis more and more. From all accounts Irene was a motherly and warm-hearted person and she never edited her speech and prided herself on speaking with a very broad Jamaican accent. One day when invited to dinner by a neighbour of hers, she replied, 'Chu me love A can't boder wit dat.' She could always create laughter and of course none of her friends took offence; this was just Irene, a character to say the least. Reggie on the other hand was meticulous in the correctness of his speech and he was a well-read and cultured man. In spite of being opposites they were a devoted couple.

Reggie had a habit of buying houses lock, stock and barrel, so when 'Fairway' could hold no more furniture he had to build a barn to store the enormous amount of purchases. It would then take him a year or two to catalogue the furniture, and at a later date he would sell these articles at a substantial profit. In the early 1920s 'Fairway' burnt down with all its contents. It was after this that he moved into Devon House.

Irene never liked the house; she found it far too large for her and as she was by then very overweight she found it difficult to walk about it. Isis did her best to still her mother's fears and assured her that she would take over the housekeeping for her. She did her best to make the beautiful old house into a home. All the antique furniture that Reggie had collected and stored over the years suited the vast rooms, but during the ownership by the Melhados Devon House never was the home that it had been to the Stiebel Jacksons. Irene never ceased to complain about its size, and Reggie of course had originally bought it for speculation.

It was during these years that Dorothy and Paul were to spend a lot of time with their grandparents at Devon House. Dorothy was then about 9 years old, and today she has cherished memories of the old house. She tells us that although she did not have any great rapport with her grandfather or grandmother, she remembers the house vividly, and recalls that she and her brother spent Saturdays there more or less 'on command' from her mother. Although Belmont Great House in which Dorothy was born, was large seen through a child's eye, she describes Devon House as 'vast'. The library was still on the left of the entrance, but the family mostly used the centre room on the ground floor and the terraced verandah at the back of the house. The room that George Stiebel had built as a ballroom, in the Melhados time, was used only occasionally for dances. Reggie and Irene liked a quiet family life and had no desire for the huge parties that the Stiebel Jacksons had given.

Dorothy today recalls that 'the two big foyers upstairs and downstairs had mostly occasional tables, a few chairs and much bric-a-brac.' The furniture Dorothy remembers were heavy mahogany pieces, part of her grandfather's collection over the years. Until the day Reggie died he employed a trained cabinetmaker-cum-carpenter to maintain the antique furniture that he was constantly buying.

Dorothy remembers that what is now an elegant courtyard surrounded by red brick buildings was then the servant's quarters and a garage and a few out-buildings. There was no back gate in the fence. All the way round the roof of the house ran a parapet which can still be seen today. It could be reached by means of a ladder-like staircase behind the back staircase. The linen closet upstairs was a room in itself by today's standards and here the children's nanny would sit, sort and stack the laundered linen.

But to Dorothy and Paul, like all children who visited Devon House, the pool was the great attraction. She describes it:

> There was what was called a plunge, this was a concrete pool, probably 10 feet by 10 feet and deep enough to come waist high on an adult...we children spent endless hours in the pool where I taught Paul to swim when he was very small.

This is the same pool that Richard Jackson enjoyed so much and where he caught his death of cold. Today, the first room protruding from the back verandah on the west side and overlooking the brick vault, is this room which is now floored over and is used as the office. She remembers a small dilapidated well where the fountain now stands but to a child's eye the main feature of the front was an enormous tree; 'a real beauty, my grandmother had a swing hung from a very high branch, and a gardener who rejoiced in the name of Rupert Elisha Duhenny was always told to swing us for as long as we required.'

The glebe lands had served as a cow pen since the patent was granted to the Rev Mr John Zellers in the late seventeenth century and up until Reggie's time there was a grass piece on the left side of the front drive. People still kept a cow or so for the family milk. The few houses in St Andrew were often surrounded by many acres of land, adequate for grazing cows. The grass piece was fenced in and mango, guava and plum trees spread their branches giving shade to the children and cows.

It was while her grandparents were living at Devon House that Dorothy reached her teens. Reggie was as keen as Isis that she be sent to school in England. While they were in England finding a school for Dorothy, the lovely Isis became ill with mastoides, an infection behind the ear and she died in London in 1928 at the age of 41.

Reggie and Irene returned to Devon House a broken-hearted couple. They had lost their only and adored daughter. Irene now declared that she was not prepared 'to run so large a house without the help of her daughter,' and eventually Reggie gave in and they moved to 'Melrose', a bungalow which he had built on Waterloo Avenue, where it still can be seen. The colossal amount of furniture from Devon House could hardly hold and Dorothy describes the bungalow as being 'stuffed with furniture.' Irene eventually refused to have any more antiques in the new house, so Reggie had to build yet another barn on 'Melrose' for storage.

But not even the move into a smaller house was to cheer Irene. Their sons, with the exception of Reggie who was not very bright,

The Melhados – a tragic family. Four of their eight children died young.

went to live in America. Reggie and Irene had now lost five of their eight children. In the First World War they had lost their son Owen while he was fighting in the Dardanelles and their sons Edmund and Donald died in an air crash. The loss of so many children hung heavily on the motherly woman and for some time she had been complaining of pain. In 1934 in the forty-eighth year of their marriage she died. By so short a time she had missed celebrating their golden wedding anniversary.

Her will is interesting, as the picture we have of Irene is of an endearing and motherly soul, not of a woman wearing beautiful jewellery, yet in her will she left many precious gems to her daughters-in-law.

When they moved to 'Melrose' Reggie had rented Devon House to Alfredo and Marjorie Grinnan. Although Alfredo was a dental surgeon, when his father died he had taken over the management of his father's sugar estates. His wife Majorie was an attractive American who was always well groomed and had an appointment with the hairdresser every week for hair, toe and fingernail grooming. In fact, she ordered that on her death the hairdresser should still perform this final task!

The Grinnans had a daughter called Mercedes and while her parents were living at Devon House she was sent to school in America. Her parents bought an apartment for her in New York. One day she washed her hair and sat in front of the gas stove to dry her long tresses. She did not realize that the stove was leaking and fell asleep, as the poisonous fumes overcame her. In the morning the young and attractive brunette was found dead. Her parents who adored her were heartbroken at losing their only child.

Those who believe in curses might say that there was surely a curse on Devon House. Misfortune had overtaken the three Stiebel Jackson girls, Reggie and Irene had lost their only daughter and three sons tragically, and now the Grinnans after only a short stay at Devon House had lost their only daughter.

After Irene's death, Reggie's greatest comfort in his loneliness was to play a great deal of bridge, a game at which he was an expert, and he continued the buying and selling of houses which was more of a game with him, although a profitable one. Reggie donated a building to St Hugh's Girls School. The head mistress, Rita Gunter Landale, describes him as 'a delightful old man with a great appreciation of literature and art. He had a wonderful sense of humour and an incredible memory, and could recite poetry endlessly. He was particularly fond of limericks and these would just pour out of him. He was most entertaining and would make you laugh from morning until night.'

As time went on Reggie became practically blind, and as he had been a great reader, the loss of his sight was a terrible affliction. He remained in good health until 14 February 1950 when he had a seizure, lost consciousness and, although he received the best medical attention, he died the following morning.

The *Gleaner* tribute to Reggie describes him as 'a retired businessman, an industrialist and Philanthropist...he was the Senior Justice of the Peace for Kingston and St Catherine...as a mark of respect the Montpelier Cigar Store and William Wilson Ltd also St Hugh's School was closed.' Rita Gunter in a statement to the *Gleaner* said, 'He will be sadly missed in the community.'

CHAPTER 5
Cecil Lindo

Cecil Lindo bought Devon House from Reginald Melhado in 1928 for his wife Agnes Irene and they lived there until he died in 1960. The property by then containing 11 acres could no longer claim the name of Penn and the Lindos simply called it 'Devon'.

Like George Stiebel, Cecil Lindo had had an adventurous career before his association with Devon House began. C.V., as he was often known, was born on 8 December 1870 in Falmouth, Trelawny, the sixth son of Frederick Lindo. They were descended from a family of Spanish Sephardic Jews who, rather than give up their Jewish faith to become Christian converts during the time of the Spanish Inquisition, decided to flee Spain. They migrated to France and prospered until the days of Napoleon Bonaparte. Family tradition says that the Emperor borrowed money from the Lindo family but while he still owed them he was forced to abdicate. The family, having helped Napoleon, feared punishment by the new ruler and decided to move north to Jersey in the Channel Islands. Thus Frederick Lindo, Cecil's father, was born a British subject and he and his brothers decided to emigrate to Jamaica.

Frederick and his brothers went into the mercantile business, stocking their shops with every imaginable item that the planters and the people of the parish would require. They did exceedingly well and it was here that Frederick met and married Grace Morales.

In time they had ten children: Augustus, Rupert, Robert, Howard, Blanche, Oscar, Cecil, Stanley, Lydia and Percy.

Unfortunately, as the young family grew up the price of sugar declined and this forced many planters to abandon their sugar crops which led to the steady decline of Trelawny's prosperity. Falmouth, the chief town, suffered heavily and where the shops had been crowded with buyers, now there were few with money in their pockets to spend. Frederick saw the fortune that he had come to seek fading into thin air.

His eldest sons needed jobs as the family was no longer prosperous enough to employ them. He cast his eyes around looking for promising prospects for his children. Kingston did not promise his sons any spectacular future, but in Portland on the east of the island, a new agricultural development had been lately started. It was the cultivation of bananas, and the fruit was shipped to the United States where it was very much in demand. Frederick advised his sons Augustus, Robert and Howard to take their savings and go to the fertile land of Portland to start a banana plantation. But agriculture depends largely on mother nature and the brothers had not reckoned with the high winds of Portland. Their hearts sank as time and time again they watched their acres of banana trees being flattened in the space of ten or fifteen minutes by strong winds. Time and time again the brothers replanted but good fortune did not follow their footsteps.

Cecil was only a boy of 12 when in 1882 his father Frederick died. His mother had little money to feed the two remaining children so later he joined his brothers who were still persevering with the developing of their banana project in Portland. But the high winds still continued to plague the parish, and not being able to reap the benefits of their labour, their savings were gradually being frittered away. When Cecil joined them, they were in despair and with their vanishing capital they felt that they were finished in Jamaica. But as so often happens, what seemed a terrible misfortune was later to prove a blessing.

In 1871 an adventurous young American, Minor Keith, joined his brothers in Costa Rica, where they were attempting to build a railway from the shanty town of Porto Limón on the low lying coastlands up through the mountains to the capital, San José. The railway was being built on a shoe-string budget and was fraught with difficulties as Porto Limón and the surrounding area at that time suffered from almost constant torrential rains. Minor Keith was on the lookout for intelligent, adventurous young men to help him in his endeavour, men who if the Keith brothers were short of ready cash would be willing to wait for their salaries. E. B. Hopkins, who had leased the Lindo brothers the Portland property, suggested that they try their luck with Keith in Costa Rica.

In 1885 Robert and Howard Lindo embarked for Costa Rica where Cecil joined them in 1889 when he was 18.

We know from Wat Stewart's book on Minor Keith that on 24 April 1889, Cecil 'received from Keith his first cheque for 40 dollars as paymaster.' Mr Keith obviously was soon aware of the young man's worth. He also employed him as a banana receiver and checker.

Four years after landing in Costa Rica, Cecil and his brothers had started planting bananas. The railway, the construction of which had cost so many lives, was a great boom to Cecil in the transportation of his bananas. The building of the first twenty five miles of the railway from Limón to San José had cost twenty five thousand lives, mainly workers from Jamaica. The length of the line was only a hundred miles but it took nineteen years to complete. It was not long before the plantations were developed and bearing fruit and Cecil was looking around for other investments. He realized that he could not depend solely on his banana plantations as he often lost much in the floods. As labourers poured in to work in the plantations and the railways, Limón expanded and more and more shacks sprang up on the outskirts of the town. With typical foresight Cecil knew that shops would soon be needed to supply the work forces with imported goods and food. He made haste to set up a small store. From their days in Falmouth the brothers knew well how to run such a shop. It was an immediate success and even in 1937 'it still stood near Porto Limón with his name boldly displayed on its facade.'

There was another development in Cecil's life which was to help him in his business adventures. He met an attractive Costa Rican girl, Caridad Quesada Lopez Calleja. There was a common belief in Jamaica that she was the president's daughter, but this was not so; she was the daughter of a very wealthy landowner. She was a lovely girl with dark hair, and Cecil, as we can see by a photograph taken by Cleary and Elliot, was a good-looking man, squarefaced, with a broad forehead and drooping mustache.

Young Cecil Lindo. 'A good looking man, square-faced with broad forehead and drooping moustache.'

Although he was only 26, he had had a most interesting life and it is no wonder that this dynamic man was able to fascinate the Costa Rican society girl. It was not long before Cecil proposed to the vivacious Caridad and they were married in 1896. By this time Cecil had built a large wooden house in the sea port and he was comfortably off, but 'comfortably off' was not enough for Cecil and of course his Costa Rican father-in-law was ready to help him in every business venture.

The properties that he had bought were thickly forested. He did not let such an asset got to waste. Lumber was needed for house building so Cecil made haste to erect a mill. The trees were felled, planks cut and there was the railway ready to transport the boards.

As this business grew, so did his family; a year after he married Caridad she had a daughter, Grace. In 1898 a second daughter, Zaira, was born.

In the meantime there was no end to Cecil's projects. With the high humidity on the Caribbean coast he realized that an ice factory would flourish and, once having the ice, his mind turned to soft drinks. What better combination, and his new project was an instant success.

Cecil's children settled well enough in Limón but they saw little of their father as he was always busy, but he never failed to look after their material comforts. Caridad would not have found it so easy to settle; a child of very wealthy parents, she must have found Limón stifling both from heat and the deprivation of the social contacts to which she had been accustomed.

Ironically, in 1907 when Cecil decided to buy a home in San José his marriage broke up, just at the time when Caridad should have been pleased to be able to live in the capital. They separated when Grace was 10 and Zaira 9. It was a trying time for the girls to adjust to their new circumstances, but at least they had the excitement of moving into the magnificent new home that their father had just bought. It was on the south edge of Parque Morazan in San José.

Grace and Zaire Lindo.

About 1907 also, Cecil and his brothers purchased a large property, Juan Vinas. This was a vast coffee and sugarcane farm near Turialba and Cecil kept buying surrounding lands that were for sale. Stanley was made the manager and the Lindo brothers eventually cultivated 12 square miles of land in that region. Cecil and Stanley developed one of the largest coffee businesses in Costa Rica and no more than a year after buying the property they were exporting 15 000 sacks of coffee. As the sugar estates flourished Cecil decided to build his own sugar refinery. He owned the whole village, streets, houses, shops and all. He decided to build a school and himself supervised the building. The school which still stands in Juan Vinas even now bears his name.

Meanwhile, Panama disease, which attacks bananas with disastrous effects, had been brought from Panama, where it had originated, into Costa Rica. No one then regarded it very seriously, but Cecil realized that with the spread of the disease land values would fall and so at this time Cecil negotiated the sale of his banana properties in Costa Rica.

On 24 April 1909, Mr Keith, representing the United Fruit Company, handed Cecil a cheque for $5 000 000 in payment for the banana interests in Costa Rica. It was an incredible achievement in the short space of twenty years for it was on 24 April 1889 that Mr Keith had paid Cecil his first cheque for $40 as his paymaster.

It was around this time that the brothers began to think seriously of once more investing in properties in Jamaica. Robert, one of Cecil's elder brothers had married a Miss Allwood and they had two sons, Leonard and Oswald, as well as a daughter, Pearl. Robert bought a property called 'Sunnyside' about 2 miles outside of Linstead. Cecil decided to send his two girls to stay with his brother Robert, who had employed a permanent governess for his children.

As his daughters were now living in Jamaica it meant that Cecil had to make several visits to the island. There was no way that he could keep his mind off expansion and development. At that time there was much talk of the very good prospects for the island's sugar industry. The cry on all sides was for the government to establish one or two factories and equip them with the latest methods of sugar manufacture. But Cecil knew that governments were slow in decision making and he was not about to wait for their lengthy discussions on the pros and cons. His quick mind saw success ahead so he immediately contacted Mr A. L. Keeling who was a large property owner. Mr Keeling had changed his name from Levy and married into the well-known Pringle family. Mr Keeling looked favourably at the project and with the Lindo brothers went straight ahead with the building of the first central sugar factory in

Jamaica, now known as Bernard Lodge on the St Catherine plain. It was not long before it proved to be a profitable enterprise.

The story goes that one day at the United Fruit Company Hotel, Myrtle Bank, Cecil had seen a lady sitting at a table, her face completely hidden by one of the fashionable large hats of those days. He was determined to see what was under the hat, so he arranged to have himself introduced. When introduced he saw a fiery Irish redhead, with bright blue eyes. Her name was Irene Dennelley and she was an Irish American. From that day the romance started. She was later to become his secretary in New York, and by 1916 he married her.

Cecil Lindo with second wife Irene on their wedding day.

There were difficulties about the marriage as both Caridad and Irene were staunch Catholics and divorce was not allowed in the Catholic Church, so to Irene's great sorrow she was not allowed to marry in the Church.

Meanwhile Cecil was still expanding his business enterprises in Jamaica. When the trustees and executors of Col Ward, a large landowner and businessman, put his entire estate on the market, Cecil decided that this was an excellent business proposition. Among the assets was the liquor firm of J. Wray and Nephew. The certificates of title show that on 23 March 1917, the Lindo brothers purchased J. Wray & Nephew and Monymusk Estates comprising Monymusk, Greenwich, Carlisle, Knights and Exeter as well as Olive Park Pen and Orange Grove Pen, all in the parish of Clarendon.

The Monymusk estate totalled 8152 acres (registered at Vol 119 Folio 81). Cecil and his brothers now owned not only the liquor business but the sugarcane estates which would keep them supplied with cane. They had paid £200 000 for J. Wray & Nephew.

Already in 1916 Cecil had bought the Appleton Estates in St Elizabeth from A. Nathan, a First World War pilot who owned one of the leading retail stores on King Street. Appleton was well watered, as the Black and the One Eye Rivers snaked across the land. It had the reputation at that time of making the best rum in the world. It was a very old sugar estate as in 1763 it was already marked on a Jamaican map. Up until 1905 the old water mill was utilised to give the estate its power, but as soon as Cecil bought it he introduced steam as the motive power for the crushing of the cane. He also bought other properties in the west of the island including Montpelier Mountain and Montpelier Wharf. He enlarged his holdings further by buying the Shettlewood Estate. He was now becoming as large a landowner in Jamaica as he was in Costa Rica.

It would appear that all Cecil's life was engrossed with expansion of his business but this was not entirely so. His second wife in the 1920s had had a baby girl who was christened Marilyn. She was a pretty child and was nicknamed Bunty by which name she was known while living in Jamaica.

At first the Lindos had lived at 'Roslin', a house beside the present Police Station on Old Hope Road, which is today part of Campion College. Later they moved to 'Odnil' which is Lindo spelt backwards. The house is on Hope Road and is now the Bob Marley Museum.

It was at the height of Cecil's success that Reginald Melhado put Devon Penn up for sale in 1928. Cecil and Irene needed no persuasion in buying the majestic old house. Here with their millions they could live and entertain in great style.

Not even their mansion on Parque Morazan in San José which had been built in 1900 and where lofty ceilings were painted by Italian artists, could compare with beautiful 'Devon' as they called the house. It was surveyed in 1927 and Cecil put the house in his wife's name, 'Agnes Irene Lindo, wife of Cecil Vernon Lindo of the Republic of Costa Rica, planter, containing eleven acres and 28 perches.' The once isolated house was now surrounded by development on all sides. It was in need of extensive repairs and Cecil gave the contract to George Hart. The bill came to £5000, which would have built two large houses at the time.

Irene took pride in the house and lightened it with pale curtains and upholstery. She was very interested in the garden; four gardeners were employed at 'Devon' and the house was full of large bowls of flowers often arranged by the owner herself. It was Irene who introduced white euphorbia into the island. She had it planted along the driveway interspersed with poinsettia and at Christmas the poinsettia bloomed red and the euphorbia was covered in fine white blooms. People from all over Kingston drove by to see the lovely display.

Irene loved to give her friends flowers and these she arranged herself. The vases were often of black or white spode and she took pleasure in arranging these before she dispatched them by her

The Drawing Room today. In the Lindo's time this was the Dining Room.

chauffeur to a favoured friend. She kept stacks of vases of every shape, and ribbons galore of every colour and holders and wires for buttonholes for the men. It was the days of evening jackets and tails and the colour of the carnation in the buttonhole would depend upon whether the invitation called for black tie or white. There was also the orchid house which had been there from the time of the Stiebel Jacksons.

Irene employed six maids including a ladies' maid. Cecil liked to give large and extravagant dinner parties. On his many trips to England, he had brought back an enormous quantity of silver. On a round table in the central hall there were six silver tea services, Cecil's secretary tells us. Irene liked to play bridge and these services were used at each table when she served tea at her ladies' bridge parties. Maids who worked with the Lindos related that there was so much silver stored in the silver vault which still stands behind the present open air restaurant, that when it was time to clean the articles, it took all the staff a full week to perform the arduous task.

Sir John Golding went to a dinner party at 'Devon' with the Cecil Lindos and he remembers being impressed with the amount of crystal and silver in the dining room, which then was the long room on the east side of the house and is now the drawing room. He recalls a lot of dark mahogany furniture. The dining room table was very big and seated at least twenty-four. The waiters were dressed in green velvet jackets and frilly shirts, each wearing white gloves. A waiter stood behind every other chair waiting to pull back the chairs for the ladies to sit, and when all were seated the endless dishes were passed around. There were six or seven courses: entrée, soup, fish, meat, dessert and savoury, coffee and, of course, the appropriate wine to go with each course. Candles in the silver candelabra lit the table with a soft light. Sir John was surprised that the plates were of gold. Many people spoke of Cecil, when lunching at the well-known Oleander Restaurant in Kingston, using a golden toothpick.

Miss May Farquharson, the daughter of Sir Arthur Farquharson, often went to these dinner parties with her father. She remembers finding it difficult to finish so many courses and at a particular dinner party when all the guests had eaten more than enough, Cecil suggested that Irene give orders for tinned peaches to be opened. When she demurred, saying that everyone was satisfied, and the guests heartily agreed with their hostess, Cecil jumped up from the table and personally saw to it that the butler produced peaches, while the replete guests secretly bewailed the fact that their hostess had been overruled. Cecil always took a keen interest in the menus and it seems extraordinary that this busy financial genius should go often to Cross Roads Market himself, to buy the weekly greens and meat.

Neville Alexander remembers that his mother and father were often guests at the 'Devon' dinner parties and he recalls that they always returned with a fabulous gift. Besides each setting there was always a present, something of gold such as a gold locket, bracelet, or gold compact and the story goes that the more beautiful the lady guest the larger the gift.

While Bunty's parents were busy giving dinner parties she was stretching up into a long-legged girl, dark haired and a tomboy, as a certain Jamaican lawyer confirms. 'When we were young I remember often playing with Bunty at "Devon". One day she fell out of one of the trees and broke her wrist in three places, and she had only fallen five feet,' he said scathingly. But he smiled, 'She had a good eye for catching a ball.' This good eye she often used to retrieve tennis balls for her half sister when she visited her father's home in San José.

In 1928, the year Cecil Lindo bought Devon House, he decided to sell his properties in St Catherine and Clarendon to the United Fruit Company. When the farms were producing five million stems of bananas annually he decided to quit banana planting. He sold his holding in the two parishes for nearly two million pounds, the largest single financial transaction in the history of Jamaica up to that time.

In that same year he bought the wine and spirit business of Daniel Finzi and Co Ltd. He was now in the liquor business in a big way. Appleton, his estate in St Elizabeth, was producing many thousands of gallons of rum and was capable of producing much more, but Cecil agreed with other rum manufacturers to restrict his production of Appleton rum to 55000 gallons each year, as an excess supply of rum on the market was causing prices to fall.

One of Cecil's attributes was that he was very generous. He was always extremely charitable; he and his wife contributed to every deserving appeal fund in Jamaica. He was the largest donor to the George V Memorial Hospital on Barbican Road, giving £500. In Who's Who in 1938 we are told that 'his philanthropies were in the region of £60000 in Jamaica alone.' This was a considerable sum at a time when a three bedroom house would cost £2000 to £3000. But not all his charities were appreciated; there was the instance when he decided to give three imposing houses to the Jamaican government, for the Attorney General, the Chief Justice and the Colonial Secretary who he thought were living in far too simple houses for their elevated station. One was a two-storey house on Lady Musgrave Road, and one the substantial house now belonging to Campion College beside the Police Station on Old Hope Road. The Colonial government of the day did not see the gift in the light that it was intended. They refused to accept the offer saying that such a present would make the country too indebted to a single individual.

His property Montpelier in St James, on the western side of the island had remained a cattle property but Cecil was not happy unless he was making a success of some new venture. He had mastered the arts of banking, flour milling, ice making and rum manufacture, and banana, cane, coffee and cocoa production, but all this was not enough for the alert mind of the 69-year-old man. He decided to go in for the production of first class beef at Montpelier. On the nine thousand acre property Cecil decided to make 5300 acres pasture land, which made Montpelier the largest single cattle property in Jamaica. In this beef breeding enterprise Cecil stocked his pastures with 3400 head of cattle. In 1938 the West India Royal Commission declared this herd the finest Mysore cattle to be seen in the world.

Cecil was not foolhardy or reckless. His business ventures were always well investigated and then built on solid foundations. During the world depression of 1929 rich men lost their money overnight and banks had to close, but Cecil's bank in Costa Rica did not crash and his many businesses were not affected.

An extraordinary facet of Cecil's character was that he was very superstitious. He would never sign a cheque on the thirteenth, and on a day when he visited Vere and saw a peacock walk across the land, he left immediately claiming that peacocks were bad luck. He would also never stay anywhere that poinciana trees grew as these, too, he held were unlucky. It was these human weaknesses and his sense of humour that made him so endearing to his friends.

The Lindos employed a young maid, Louise White, who was often given the task of looking after Bunty; Louise was young enough to enjoy playing with her employer's daughter. She often climbed trees with her and it was her regular duty after lunch to take Bunty upstairs to rest and at three o'clock Louise would return to help the young girl dress for the afternoon. She tells us that Bunty was a well-behaved girl and she had a German governess who travelled with the Lindos wherever they went.

Louise worked for many years with the Lindos. She says that Cecil, Irene and Bunty each had their own car and chauffeur. There was also a market car. Her mistress had a personal maid who laid out her clothes for her and if she was ill stayed by her employer's side all day. Like the Stiebel Jacksons they had a large staff, two cooks, two laundresses, two waitresses, two housemaids and six gardeners and sometimes there was a housekeeper. With such as staff, 'Devon' was beautifully kept.

Louise speaks of Irene as being a very kind person. If any of the staff displeased her, she asked her husband to deal with the matter. Louise was devoted to her employers and was ruffled at any trace of criticism of the Lindos. She found Cecil kind and gentle and recalls that he was always ready to listen to anything that the staff had to say or would grant them a favour, and if they were short of money they could ask Cecil to give them an advance on their salary. Louise can remember asking him one day if she could borrow £20. Each week she repaid a certain amount and when she had returned £8 she said one week, 'Mr Cecil, you can take £5 this week.' His reply was, 'No, you are a good girl, you can keep the balance owing.' She recalls that he was always ready to help the poor and on his trips to the market he often bought vegetables or fruit for the staff. At Christmas they were treated to a turkey, ham and plum pudding dinner, and they were all given big presents. Sometimes their employers sent them to see a movie. After a dinner party Louise says that 'Mr Cecil always came into the kitchen and said, "Girls you have done well," and he would give each of us £2 which was then a lot of money.'

The maid recalls the big parties that were given for Bunty on her birthdays when one hundred or more guests came, both young and old. There was a variety of food and there was dancing to gramophone records in the ballroom upstairs. The ballroom had the beautiful chandelier which is still to be seen there today and there were tall gilt mirrors on the east and west walls. The ballroom at this time was furnished as a formal drawing room with Louis XV gilded furniture. Touring in France, Irene had admired the Louis XV furniture in a chateau which they had visited. Some months after their return to Jamaica a van appeared at Devon House and when the contents were unpacked Irene was surprised to see all the gilded furniture that she had admired. Cecil had told her nothing as he had wanted to surprise her. Even after thirty years of marriage they remained a devoted couple; Cecil at home called his wife affectionately 'Mamsie' and she called him 'Papsie'.

The magnificent Ballroom.

The party that impressed Louise the most was one which the Lindos gave after the opening of the Carib Theatre in 1938. That was the great social event of the day. Metro Goldwyn Mayer films had not been shown in Jamaica for many years as the film company, the Palace Amusement Co, owned by Mr Audley Morais, had had a disagreement with them. As their films were very good, Mr Billy Cargill and Mr B.M. Andrade built the Carib Cinema to show mainly MGM films. It was the first building to be air-conditioned in the island.

The opening night was by invitation only; all the social set of Kingston and St Andrew attended. The men wore dinner jackets and the women wore their loveliest evening gowns. The great pianist, Arthur Rubinstein, had been invited to play at the opening. In fact it was a disaster as the air-conditioner did not work on the first night and everyone sweltered. After the show the VIPs were invited to a supper and ball at 'Devon'. Louise remembers the announcer dressed in livery and tapping his poll as he announced each guest and champagne flowed. Rubinstein was also invited to the party and he played the inlaid Steinway grand piano that stood in the east corner of the ballroom.

The old maid recalls that Irene took an interest in the running of the house when there was a party. She would write down what china and crystal were to be used and she herself would prepare some of the sauces. This was unusual in those days as many of the hostesses in Kingston did not even know how to boil an egg and relied solely on their excellent cooks.

One of the sorrows of Irene's life was that she had not been married in the Catholic Church, but when the first Mrs Lindo died in Italy, Cecil and Irene were at last able to have a church wedding and Louise remembers them going to Holy Cross to be quietly married. At some time Cecil became a Catholic convert, but we don't know the exact date.

In Cecil's time at 'Devon', the room on the west side of the enclosed front verandah was his library and office. Large bookcases lined the walls on the south and west and Cecil sat behind a large desk. When Louise was asked what he did with his time after selling out his various businesses she laughed and said, 'He spent all day finding out how he could make money grow.'

Cecil and Irene's bedroom was the room on the east, which is shown today as the master bedroom. They had two four poster mahogany beds, but without canopies. The small room behind the staircase which had been Mrs Jackson's boudoir was used in the Lindos' time as Cecil's den, where he had his radio and leather couch and chairs. Bunty's room was the large room on the west side, and the room beside it was a guest room where Bunty's friends often spent a night or two. The small room on the west side of the ballroom was still used as a sewing room where the ladies' maid checked the laundry and mended the clothes.

Irene always came downstairs for breakfast on the back verandah. After lunch she went to rest, and at four o'clock tea was taken up to her bedroom. Then the couple dressed and went down to the east verandah 'to hold court' as in those days after 4.30 p.m. it was accepted that callers came to visist. On an afternoon when there were no callers sometimes they went for a drive to Hope Gardens or along the Palisadoes Road. There was less traffic on the roads in those days and driving was a pleasant pastime.

In 1939 Cecil sold out most of his businesses in Jamaica. He had already sold the Clarendon and St Catherine estates to the United Fruit Company and now he sold Wray and Nephew and Appleton Estates to his brother Percy. He kept Montpelier and Shettlewood for his pet beef-producing project and he also kept Greenwich in the hills of St Andrew.

Bunty had been sent to school at Mount Mary College, New York, and she had grown into a very pretty girl. No sooner had she left school than a young American fell in love with her. My own sister, Beryl, and her financé Gus Desnoes were seeing off friends who were sailing to America. They were talking to Philip Yawman, a friend of Gus Desnoes, when Bunty Lindo passed on an upper

The Master Bedroom.

Theresa Steibel Jacksons boudoir later used by Cecil Lindo as his den.

deck. Philip, who had never seen her before, looked up and said to Beryl, 'There is the girl I am going to marry,' and true enough within a few months he married her. The Yawmans were a well-known and wealthy American family for Philip's father and grandfather had been in the steel business.

Bunty Lindo.

Sometime later Bunty had a son also christened Philip. Today he still refers to his Lindo grandfather as 'Gramps' and he writes, 'I have always felt a particular affinity for him, perhaps because I was the only grandchild of his second marriage.' Sometimes he came to stay with his grandparents at 'Devon', and once a year the Lindos visited their daughter in Rochester where she and her husband lived. Today Cecil's grandson Philip has three sons of his own.

Cecil spent his last years very happily at 'Devon'. Every morning his secretary came up to the house and he sat on the verandah outside the library dictating letters. He kept a close watch on his investments in London and New York. He suffered a great deal from gout and had to have his shoes specially made higher on one side, so as to ease his pain. He lived to see the 1951 hurricane which did great damage to Kingston. We do not know if 'Devon' was damaged, but some of the mains of Kingston and St Andrew were broken and so many people had no water. Cecil opened his gates to any one who was short of water as the 'Devon' wells were still giving a good supply.

In the last years of his life Cecil was ailing, and he died at 'Devon' of a heart attack in June 1960 at the age of 89. The *Daily Gleaner* report reads: 'He grew into a railway magnate, banker and holder of vast banana plantations, sugar, coffee and cocoa estates. His holdings in Jamaica alone, not counting Costa Rica, were so large that it would need a book to give details of them all.' All the original books and ledgers of his business dealings are to be found today at the Archives in Spanish Town. The funeral service was held at the Holy Cross Church, Half Way Tree, and he was buried at the Immaculate Conception Chapel at Stony Hill.

Cecil's will was short and to the point:

> I appoint my wife Agnes Irene Lindo and my daughter Zaira Murray executors and trustees.... I declare that all the contents of my wife's residence in Jamaica known as 26 Hope Road, St Andrew belong to her absolutely being her property not mine.... I give and bequeath all my property of whatsoever nature and wheresoever situated

Cecil Lindo in later life. He was the last private owner of Devon House.

equally between my said wife and my three daughters being my only children Zaira Murray, Grace Lindo and Marilyn Lindo for their own use absolutely.

This will was dated 26 August 1938.

Irene lived for another eight years mostly in New York. Sometime in 1965 she was approached by developers and she decided to sell 'Devon'. Burnett Webster, a lover of things beautiful hearing that the developers were planning to destroy the old house and build a block of apartments similar to Abbey Court tried to stop the sale going through. When he failed in his efforts he even thought of offering to buy Devon House. In desperation he reported the matter to the Minister of Welfare and Development, the Hon Edward Seaga who agreed that this beautiful house could not be bulldozed by developers, so he placed a restriction order on the property, under the National Trust Act. We read in the *Daily Gleaner* of 27 August 1965:

'The Hon Edward Seaga has served an Interim Preservation Notice on the building known as Devon House ... the finest 19th century residence remaining in the island. In addition to the main building there are out buildings which are older than the main buildings and containing some of the finest ovens and other brick work of the period. The Interim Notices are served by the Minister under the law when he considers that a monument is in danger of destruction, removal or damage and remains effective for a period of 21 months .... Steps are then taken during the period to ensure the preservation of the building.'

It was a trying time for Irene with the developers and the government haggling over 'Devon', but finally a settlement was reached.

With 'Devon' sold there was now nothing to keep Irene in Jamaica. All the silver, crystal, china and furniture that was in the house was shipped to America where she lived at her home on Fifth Avenue in New York, until she died. Her faithful Louise went with her and cared for her in her last days. She suffered from a heart condition, but she was happy to be near her daughter and grandson and Louise recalls that she phoned Bunty many times a week. In 1968 she died of a stroke.

She and Cecil were the last private owners of Devon House.

CHAPTER 6
Devon House – Modern History

As soon as the sale of Devon House, as it was now called, was final, the Minister of Development the Hon Edward Seaga ordered the restoration of the building. The task was given to Tom Concannon, an English architect working with the Town Planning Department. He was a man with a great feel for history and especially for old buildings.

Tom Concannon was born in London in 1906. He studied architecture at the Central London Polytechnic and later became a Fellow of the Royal Town Planning Institute. His first job took him to Palestine where he was architect and field archaeologist for Megiddo. He then worked in Nigeria and in Hong Kong later, where during the Second World War, he was made a prisoner of war by the Japanese. Tom admitted that this had been a grim experience, but in describing it he said he 'gave lectures on the pyramids, taught at the school they set up and designed buildings for other interns for when they got out.' He was a man with a great deal of experience in his field. At the end of the war he returned to Jerusalem and was put in charge of the maintenance of the Holy Places. He worked on the Dome of the Chain and the Church of the Holy Sepulcher. He also worked in Borneo and Malaya.

He helped in founding the Malayan Institute of Architects of which he was made a life member. After this interesting life he retired and took a job in Jamaica, working with the National Trust as Technical Director. 'Old Tom' was what his staff called him behind his back. He was a plump man and wore the most ill-fitting clothes and he used a monocle when he wanted a closer look at detail. All who worked for him spoke of his encyclopedic knowledge which went with a photographic memory.

In Jamaica we owe Tom a particular debt of gratitude for the many historical sites and buildings which he restored, including buildings at Port Henderson which was the sea port of Spanish Town when it was the capital of Jamaica, buildings in Spanish Town, and the Naval Hospital at Port Royal which is now a museum for the relics which have been retrieved from the seventeenth century sunken city at Port Royal. He also restored Fort Charles, where England's famous Admiral Lord Nelson walked the decks when he was a young lieutenant, and Rose Hall Great House in St James. It is to the fact that Tom was a perfectionist that we owe the excellent restoration of our beautiful Devon House.

Tom Concannon.

While Tom carried out his work on Devon House he lived frugally in one room at Liguanea Club. His work was his life and the buildings that he restored were always done with authenticity and taste, but in the course of achieving this he often drove people to distraction, 'because by being a stickler for truth and protocol he could be exceedingly dogged and pedantic.'

Tom, in an article described Devon House as he found it in 1967 as 'probably the most impressive house built in Jamaica . . . solidly constructed in brick and timber. Devon House is a striking piece of domestic architecture in a classical style and on a scale larger than comparable buildings in the island.' Because George Stiebel was not an architect, Tom did not believe that he could have been capable of drawing the plans of Devon House. 'It is more likely,' he said, 'that he had seen a similar house in his travels, and had made sketches or obtained drawings.' After a lapse of over one hundred years there is no way to tell whether Tom was right or whether George did make the design independently. Tom describes the house as being,

> a rectangular block on two floors with two timber interval stairways, one to the west in an entrance vestibule or long hall on the south front and second place (sic) at the rear north. This principal stairway is approached by an inner hall flanked by a dining room east and library, including bedrooms and staff rooms and a pantry and kitchen. There is a wine cellar under the north stairs. The first floor contains bedrooms, bathrooms, a small library or study, and a large salon with parquet floor, papered dado and cornice in wood with plaster roundels. The rectangular ceiling is decorated with fibrous plaster reliefs and a chandelier is hung from the centre, this chandelier seems to have been a fixture of the house from the beginning. It hangs from the ceiling unifying a room of impressive size. Above the roof, is an attic which provides storage space, the roof is of pine timber, covered in shingles.

When the government bought Devon House, it had been over twenty years since Cecil Lindo had commissioned George Hart to

Devon House in 1966 before the first restoration.

repair the buildings, and after he died, Irene had gone to live in New York, so during that period the house had stood for the most part empty. When Tom Concannon took over the restoration he found every imaginable type of termite in the old wood. The old buildings on the eastern side which are now craft shops were then the maids' quarters and the kitchen was the same as at present. These were in relatively good condition, but the outbuildings on the western side were dilapidated. Here the former coach house had been the garage and the buildings behind had been the chauffeur's quarters and the gardeners' living area. The roof of these had gone.

Ray McIntyre from the Public Works Department had been seconded to help Tom with the restoration and was given the task of remodelling these outbuildings under the 'Master's meticulous eye,' as Ray said wryly. The coach house was enlarged and prepared

Buildings on the East side formerly maid's quarters and kitchen.

to be used as an English type tavern, the old kitchen was restored to be used for cooking the meals for the outdoor restaurant and the staff quarters behind were restored and prepared for displaying the local crafts and the furniture made at 'Things Jamaican.' Tom had promised to have the restoration accomplished by early 1968 when the house was due to be opened to the public. He supervised every detail of the restoration and repairs, and although Ray was in charge of the outbuildings, Tom still kept a watchful eye on the work. Often he would draw the mortise and tenon joint or whatever he was demanding of his workmen on the wall!

Tom Concannon died in 1974. When Devon House was refurnished for the second time in the Victorian style and opened again to the public in 1984, 10 years later, various societies erected a plaque on the front verandah to honour him for his work on the restoration and conservation of Jamaican buildings. The then Governor,

One of the Things Jamaican Craft Shops on the west side.

Sir Florizel Glasspole, unveiled the plaque, which is of aluminium and engraved with these words:

> In memory of T. A. L. Concannon, C.D.F., I.B.M., F.S.A., M.T.P.I. 1905–1974. His life displayed the maxim 'Whatever is worth doing is worth doing well.' Jamaica where he made his last home 1959–1974 and particularly our societies are richer for his high standard and dedicated service. The Archaeological Society of Jamaica, the Jamaica Institute of Architects, the Jamaica Georgian Society, the Jamaica Historical Society, December 1984.

Mr Edward Seaga who had saved the house from the developer's hand took a keen interest in the work being done and he decided that he must have an expert interior decorator to furnish the building. He was introduced to Mr Sergio Dello Strologo, an Italian design consultant attached to the UN, who had worked in Iran, Burma, Greece, Israel and Florence.

There was much discussion as just what to make of the old house and it was decided that as 'Things Jamaican' was concentrating on making furniture, the house would be an ideal place to display reproductions of various periods of furniture and of items found at Port Royal. The committee chose the Cromwellian, Queen Anne and Georgian periods. They also decided to display Jamaican antiques and appealed for donations of these to be given to Devon House.

Now that the course was set, feverish activities started at 'Things Jamaican'. Old books were consulted for every detail of the period furniture and mahogany reproductions were made. Peter Cave, an Englishman who was in Jamaica at the time, working with the procelain factory, copied the blue and white seventeenth century pottery which had been found in Port Royal for display in the house. The committee also decided to have the pewter spoons, forks, plates and tankards that had been discovered at Port Royal copied and put on display.

The front anteroom on the west side of the ballroom was called the Hakewill Room as it displayed twelve aquatints of Jamaica by James Hakewill done in 1820–1821.

In the adjoining room called the Belisario Room, some of Belisario's prints were displayed. Belisario was a Jamaican Jew who in 1837 published a book of drawings of Negro customs and life. Four of these were hung on the walls of this small room and were lit by the Venetian Mureno chandelier which Sergio and his wife had donated. The prints were of John Canoe festivities.

It was decided that the carriage house would be the most suitable building for the bar and now it was left to Sergio to cope with the design of the interior furnishings. The intention was to furnish the tavern in the period of William and Mary with heavy high-backed chairs and tables, rustic benches and high stools at the bar.

Driving through Spanish Town one day Sergio had noticed a man who did very fine carvings. Mulling over the design for the

The Jamaican handcrafted lion rampant carved from mahogany that has roared over the Grog Shoppe since 1967

tavern, he decided to use the figurehead from the ancient Swedish Viking Ship, *Vasa*. It was a lion rampant and Sergio had a book with a picture of this figurehead, and remembering the carver in Spanish Town, he took the book to him and gave him the order to carve a replica in mahogany. A month or so later, Sergio went to see how the carving was getting along. It was finished, but to his disappointment the carver had made a flat carving. Sergio explained that he had wanted a lion to look real in three dimensions. The carver assured the Italian that he could do this, and told him when he could send for the lion. Sergio went away very doubtful as to whether he could get what he wanted. In due course the carving was sent for and was far better than Sergio had ever hoped it would be. Even Tom had to admit that it was magnificent and he volunteered to make a stone pediment for it with a chain to hold it in place so that it did not fall on the heads of any of the patrons. It was decided to call the tavern the Port Royal Grog Shoppe.

The red brick building with its double gabled roof is decorated with white fretwork and is in marked contrast to the white house. The very large arched door dates from George Stiebel's time; carriages stood much higher than cars so we enter a high ceilinged room. The huge bar is surrounded by a natural dark wooden counter, and on one wall hangs the blue and white plates copied from those found at Port Royal. There are copper carriage lamps with their reflectors and brown pottery mugs above the counter.

On the west wall is a print of a proclamation of Charles II urging planters to go to 'His Majesties island of Jamaica,' dated 1661, a fitting proclamation for the tavern, built as it is on the land that King Charles II had patented to John Zellers. On the same wall hangs an old print donated by Tom Concannon, a scene of Port Royal in 1692 when the earthquake struck. Outside the tavern is the patio overlooking which is the balcony where George Stiebel used to have breakfast with Governor Sir Henry Blake. On the verandah below, today many wedding receptions are held. Sergio Dello Strologo tells us that on one weekend, one hundred wedding parties were counted. And Mr Edward Seaga remembers sitting on the balcony in the 1960s and watching two brides jostling each other to be first with the photographer. 'It got so bad,' he said, 'that one took off her shoes and threatened the other bride.'

On the north side of the patio still stands the brick vault, now softened by an exotic creeper and under a magnificent mahogony tree. Here tourists and locals often dine under the stars. Behind the coach house are the ancient kitchens which had belonged to the rectory, modernized for the preparation of dishes for the restaurant. The waiters are suitably dressed in jerkins, white shirts and knee breeches, only sadly missing are the buckles on their very modern shoes.

Exterior of the Grog Shoppe. Note the large arch doors to the right of the picture which date from George Stiebel's time.

For the first restoration in the 1960s, the verandahs of the house were lighted by large brass lanterns which were Williamsburg reproductions. Inside were nineteenth century Oriental rugs which Sergio Dello Strologo picked up in New York, a Khiva Bukhara rug with elephant foot design, and Baluchistan, Kharassan and antique Herez rugs. He also chose brocade and upholstering material to blend with the carpets. Unfortunately, these carpets disappeared in the 1970s when Devon House was made the National Gallery and they have never been found.

People started donating antiques to the old house. Among them, Tom Concannon gave an old Jamaican four-poster bed with two interlocking posts carved out of one piece of mahogany. When the National Gallery was established, this bed and other pieces of furniture were sent to Iter Boreale in St Mary which housed antique Jamaican furniture on display to the public. Sad to say the house burnt down with all the furniture in it.

The Institute of Jamaica provided original portraits of various early governors and prominent Jamaican citizens. The room on the west of the entrance called the Conquest Room housed furniture from the period 1655–1701, Cromwell, Charles II, and William and Mary. In this room was a painting of Oliver Cromwell believed to be a contemporary copy of the full-length portrait in the National Gallery in London. In a glass case was a highly ornate silver and gold chancellor's purse and the broad seal of Jamaica. Prior to 1880 the governor of Jamaica was ex-officio chancellor of the island, and on state occasions, the chancellor's purse was carried before him by the Registrar of the Court of Chancery and laid on the table at which he sat. Its purpose was to hold the broad seal of the island of which the governor, as chancellor, had charge.

The ballroom upstairs was named the Patriots Salon, and there was the Edward Jordan room.

The 'Port Royal Grog Shoppe' and two craft shops were opened by Mrs Seaga, unbuckling a buccaneer's belt on 23 January 1968. Mr Seaga elaborated on his plans for Devon House as an art centre, which would display both new and old Jamaican works. In the main house he planned to have poetry readings and concerts. He proposed to make the gardens show off Jamaican flora and fruit, and besides two orchid houses, also an aviary of Jamaican birds. These plans have not materialized.

The house itself was officially opened by Edward Seaga who described it as 'a one stop exhibition of Jamaican culture.' Amongst those who attended were the Governor-General Sir Clifford Campbell and Sir Alexander Bustamante.

There was a delightful article in the *Gleaner* about the guidettes and the plans of the future. 'Among the attractions of Devon House are the old world costumes worn by the guidettes, the girls who conduct the tours of the house and its furnishings. These girls and staffers are also seen in a twice weekly cabaret. The costumes have an interesting history.' These were copied from the Belisario prints by Sally Lopez. The guidettes were set the task of discovering the

Mr. Seaga opening Devon House.

historical background of the house. From this research Mrs Carmen Manley composed a talk with which the guidettes regaled the visitors. She also organized a theatre group of the employees called the Devon House Players.

The Players were trained in creative dancing by the well-known dance teacher Lavinia Williams, who also did the choreography for the group's first production. Olive Lewin, then music research officer of the Jamaica School of Music, also volunteered to train the group in singing old plantation songs and religious songs. 'Gertrude Sherman a former beauty queen who worked with the National Dance Jamaica Company is continuing the training and choreography,' said a *Gleaner* report. Carmen Manley tried to create a united front and sense of loyalty amongst the staff and described it as 'a real family affair.' Archie, Flower Stick, Congo and Pocomania dances were performed. The dialect selections were written by the distinguished Jamaica folklorist Louise Bennett.

On 19 October 1968, five new shops were opened. Mr Seaga in his address emphasized the importance of cottage industries to the island as they provided working opportunities for the young women who made up most of the unemployed population. He appealed to designers in the island to use the 'Things Jamaican' project as an outlet for their goods. A fashion show followed, featuring some of the designs in the new shops.

Jewellery and pewter cutlery reproductions were displayed for sale in the old red brick vault. The sales in this shop were very slow so it was eventually closed. However it has recently been re-opened.

The critical Jamaican public soon had a scathing name for Devon House. It was called 'The National toothache', but we are glad to say that a Mrs A. R. Walcott in a letter to the *Gleaner* on 22 November 1968 defended the project. She wrote, 'In my humble opinion Devon House is worth every penny of the money which has been spent on it and I congratulate all who have made this project accessible to Jamaicans for a modest three shillings.' On 11 May 1971, an American visitor said that Americans complain of many countries as 'Gyp' but at that time he said that Jamaica was relatively free of this accusation. He wrote of Devon House:

> After Blue Mountain Inn it is definitely the most attractive place in Kingston at which to eat. The lunch, soup and entrée start at $1.50. Dinner is a $3.50 affair and well worth it. Wednesday there is a buffet and Saturday a barbecue with a choice of four main courses .... You are not likely to be crowded out as a Devon House staffer says most local diners do not like hopping up and down. The staff complained of lack of support, and say the locals say the reason is that Jamaican food is what they eat at home and not on an evening out. The other is that if anyone eats at night in the open air, dew will soak you, which Jamaicans consider unhealthy.

In 1972 the People's National Party led by Mr Michael Manley won at the polls. Mr Manley's mother Mrs Edna Manley, an internationally-known sculptor and artist, had been appealing for a National Gallery for Jamaica since the 1930s. In 1974 the new government decided that Devon House was to become the National Gallery. The antique and reproduction furniture was partly stored in one of the rooms at Devon House and some was sent to the Institute of Jamaica on East Street.

There were a lot of alterations to be done on Devon House to prepare it for use as an art gallery. The beautiful old building was full of windows and doors which left little room to display paintings, so partitions had to be built on which to hang them. The old walls had to be prepared for the hanging of many landscapes and portraits, then there was the lighting of those displayed. So in came the electricians.

At last the house was ready and the Institute of Jamaica handed over their collection of 200 paintings and 30 pieces of sculpture in 1974 to the National Gallery at Devon House. Amongst these were a fair number of masterpieces. The ground floor accommodated regular shows, and at least six times a year exhibitions were organized. The second floor displayed the Jamaican collection which was then valued at two million dollars.

A year after the National Gallery opened, it acquired the services of a brilliant young Jamaican, Mr David Boxer, as curator. Born in 1946, David attended Calabar High School and Jamaica College and then he went on to Cornell University in the USA where he attained his BA in 1969. Later he attended Johns Hopkins University where he achieved his MA in 1972. He went on to acquire a Phd in Art History in 1975. Not only was he a scholar but a painter and sculptor as well. He remains curator to this day.

On 15 March 1981 a *Gleaner* supplement reported that there were shows six times a year in different categories...

> There are namely, a retrospective show honouring a specific Jamaican artist and showing the finest representatives of his or her life's work. People like Carl Abrahams, John Dunkley, the supreme Jamaican artist, Karl Parboosingh, Albert Huie and Edna Manley

have been featured. The annual national exhibition reflects the state of art in Jamaica, as all artists are invited to submit work done during the past year to a panel of judges who select exhibits. The exhibition was started by the Institute and taken over by the Gallery in 1977 at which time drawing, sculpture and ceramics were added to the usual fare of paintings. The Thematic Series like the Passion of Christ concentrate on special artistic themes and historical exhibitions such as the Formative years 1922–40.... Foreign exhibitions were usually held once every year, and a collectors series in which corporate institutional works not accessible to the public are shown.... 'The latter series helps to develop collectors,' said Dr Boxer. 'In fact you could say I collect collectors, and a few private collections have already been committed to the Gallery when their owners die.'

The Gallery showed a variety of art forms; traditional to primitive, academic and abstract, all found a place there. Although the curator was anxious to purchase more Jamaican paintings, for they only bought from Jamaican artists, other Caribbean works were purchased with donations. In 1980–81 the government was very short of funds and the budget allotted to the Gallery was only $268 000 of which $25 000 was to purchase new works. As major Dunkleys and Parboosinghs were selling for $10 000 each we realize the slimness of the allotment. The Gallery depended on the rentals of the craft shops, the Grog Shoppe, the restaurant and on donations to augment its funds. The Annual Exhibition was the only selling show.

As the collection grew David Boxer realized the inadequacies of Devon House as an Art Gallery. Erecting too many partitions on which to hang the paintings had created a heat problem for no longer could the cool air blow freely throughout the house, and when there was a crowd the heat became unbearable. They were unable to take international exhibitions, as a wooden building was considered a high fire risk and no insurance company would cover the possible losses. Also David wrote of a lack of 'humidity control which is necessary to preserve certain delicate works.' When there was a popular exhibition, a problem arose in that only eighty people should be on the top floor at any one time. There was also a question of storage space for the expanding collection. The year before they had actually built a safe store room to house the important works from the collection. The entire contents had to be evacuated prior to hurricane Allen as they had been advised that the entire roof could be blown off, if the hurricane passed directly over Kingston.

Following Mr Seaga's victory at the polls in October 1980, he decided that he wished to see Devon House furnished on the lines of a nineteenth century Jamaican Great House, so a building on Orange Street was found for the National Gallery.

Sergio Dello Strologo was brought back to refurbish the interior. Unfortunately there was no Tom Concannon to call upon as he had died, but the Jamaican architect, Ray McIntrye, who had worked with Tom on the previous repairs, was available to take up the task of restoring the building from a gallery to that of a private dwelling which would be opened to the public.

Two of the former crew were now back at Devon House and Mr Seaga recruited the services of an excellent Jamaican interior decorator, Mrs Dorit Hutson, to help with the refurnishing of the old house. Ray was involved in removing the partitions and electric wiring which had been installed when the house was the National Gallery. He also extended the back terrace to form a coffee shop which now serves Jamaican coffee in seven different styles as well as snacks such as the popular lobster and chicken patties.

While Ray was busy with the extensions Sergio went to America to find replacements for the lost carpets. He found a Welshman in New York who sold second-hand oriental carpets and here he was able to buy a Kermanshah, a Meshed and two Hamadans also a persimmon red Turkish carpet. The large one in today's drawing room cost US$2000. The house was being furnished in the period of 1860–70 and these carpets were in keeping with that time.

Above, *the popular Coffee Terrace and,* left, *the Brick Oven.*

Opposite: *The Brick Oven's restored kitchen.*

Dorit started her arduous search for Jamaican and Caribbean antiques; the reproductions that Things Jamaican had made were also used, wherever they fitted in with the period. Of course there were some European imports, as well off Jamaicans had always had a sprinkling of imported period furniture in their homes. Sergio looked for antiques in Barbados and Trinidad and the Rev Philip Hart, the Director of the Institute of Jamaica, took a keen interest in the finding of Jamaican antiques.

Mrs Hutson busied herself too with deciding on curtains which would blend with the carpets that Sergio had purchased in New York. It was at Schumacher in New York that she found some of the wall paper and materials which were right for the Victorian period.

Mr Karl (Jerry) Craig, Director of Industrial Designs at Things Jamaican restored the kitchen on the east and even got the ovens working again so now we can buy the most delicious fresh bread and other goodies which are baked in the old ovens. The crystal chandelier in the ballroom dating from George Stiebel's time was found broken in two parts. Luckily there was an engineer, John Thompson, working for APEC whose hobby was restoring chandeliers and he was asked to restore the broken pieces. The

The splendid ballroom chandelier.

problem was that it was difficult to find the correct glass pendants and crystal chains and 'old types of triangles and beautiful pendants, remnants of English chandeliers of the period.' Peter Hauffe, a former teacher at the Royal College of Arts, set about searching antiquarian shops in Sussex in England; Dorit joined the search and found some in Falmouth, which Ray Fremmer had collected and Sergio was able to add to the collection on visits to Trinidad and Barbados. At last the enthusiast was able to restore the chandelier to its former splendour and this is the one which today adorns the ballroom.

Mr Robin Morris did the restoration of the antique furniture which Dorit had found. During repairs Sergio had discovered that what had been thought to be Wedgwood porcelain plaques decorating the ceiling of the ballroom, after testing and scraping, were in fact a form of hard plaster. This had been painted green. The cleaning showed that the plaster plaques were indeed a lovely Wedgwood blue and the cleaning also exposed more detail.

The Italian statues of the four seasons were placed in the eastern garden, having over the years lost the prominent position in front of the house that George Stiebel had given them.

The work at Devon House continued at a furious pace on all sides as on 6 December 1982, Mr Seaga announced during the official opening of the seven Devon House craft shops that the restoration and beautification of Devon House was to be completed in time for the Queen's visit early the following year. Mr Seaga spoke of great plans for the old house which, although the government was short of funds, were to be made possible through a loan from the IDB and with the assistance of designers and craftsmen from abroad through the United Nations Development Programme. They planned to train local craftsmen and to market the work that they produced at Devon House.

Two days before the Queen was to dine at Devon House, chaos still reigned and the old house was by no means ready to receive her and there was not nearly enough furniture. Everywhere artisans were at work. In the now elegant palm room with its panelling of palms painted on cotton, the Jamaican artist Angela Staples was at work. When the original Scalamandre silk-screened fabric chosen from a catalogue had arrived, Sergio and Dorit had been horrified at the brightness of the colours so they had hurriedly asked Angela to repaint the panels with such flowers as hibiscus and orchids, decorated with butterflies. On close inspection we find each panel is slightly different but of pastel shades which are most pleasing and in keeping with the antique furniture.

The frame of the Venetian mirror in the drawing room was being touched up by Sergio himself, a carpenter was putting the finishing touches to some of the wood work, and a cabinet maker was repolishing.

A day before the Queen arrived, even some of the curtains were not yet in place and it appeared an impossible task to have the house ready by the following day, but as the day proceeded the pace of work accelerated to meet the deadline. On the very day, vans of furniture kept arriving and cars were constantly rolling in with antiques lent to the old house for the Queen's visit. Flowers were brought in from the countryside and flower arrangers who had volunteered their services were at work. The atmosphere at Devon House was of a family all putting their best foot forward to make an important family occasion a success. As evening approached the beautiful floral arrangements were placed in each room and the whole house looked simply splendid.

The Jamaican senior police officers and the army's chief officers had all inspected the security, but at the last minute, as dusk approached, the Queen's security officers inspecting the east verandah where the table was laid for the royal couple to dine exclaimed, 'Her Majesty can't possibly dine here. She is in full view of the house opposite, someone could take a pot shot at her.' There was momentarily panic, for how could they possibly at this late hour reset and relocate the whole table. Just at that time someone solved the problem with the idea of gigantic potted plants to hide the Queen from view.

The Queen and her husband Prince Philip had been in the island for a four-day visit. It was on Tuesday, 15 February 1983, the evening before the tour ended, that they invited their Jamaican hosts to dinner at Devon House. It was over three hundred years since her Stuart ancestor King Charles II had patented the glebe lands to John Zellers on the 6 May 1667. This was the first time that a reigning monarch had visited the property.

The royal couple were met on the white marble front steps by Mr and Mrs Seaga, and Her Majesty's representative, the Governor-General Sir Florizel Glasspole and Lady Glasspole. Mr Seaga then presented the leading personalities of Devon House and the culture sphere to them.

Mr and Mrs Seaga escorted the Queen and her husband through

The Queen's visit.

the house. The tour guides were Mr Dello Strologo and Mrs Hutson who were kept busy answering questions posed by the royal couple. The Queen was most interested in the portrait of Col Peter Beckford in his elegant coat and breeches. He was Lieutenant Governor of Jamaica in 1720. He was also President of the Council and first Custos of Kingston. He had owned twenty-two plantations and nearly four thousand slaves. He died leaving £100 000 in personal property and he was deemed one of the richest West Indian proprietors. The portrait of this gentleman hangs in the dining room of today. The Queen did not fail to admire the Georgian Caribbean cellaret for holding wines and liqueurs. It is a rare piece and was found in one of the other West Indian islands. The royal couple were most intrigued with the American nineteenth century dining room table, which had been lent by Mr Hugh Hart. It was an unusual table, the method of extension to its full length was that of an accordion. Her Majesty said that she had never seen a table like it and she was so interested that she knelt to see how a fourteen foot table could be folded to such a compact size. After walking through the rooms downstairs they mounted the front staircase to the ballroom. At the grand piano Orrett Rhoden was playing selections from Chopin and Shubert.

George Stiebel's chandelier sparkled as it was reflected in the large gilt mirror and lit the pastel shades of the room. As Prince Philip stood in the doorway, he looked up at the ceiling with a puzzled expression and said, 'But I have seen this room before, only it was different.' Sergio was at his side and said, 'Yes Sir, you have been here before. The Prime Minister brought you here in 1971 when you were on a semi-official visit, but the house has been re-furbished.'

The royal couple then moved into what is now called the ladies' sitting room. They moved on into the young ladies' bedroom and the Queen admired the Meissen chandelier and said that she had

The young ladies bedroom with its beautiful Meissen chandelier.

one like it at Sandringham Castle. Dorit had been lucky enough to find this one in a Jamaican antiquarian collection on the north coast. The chandelier was in perfect condition and is a most beautiful example of Meissen porcelain. The Queen also admired the Shumacher chintz curtains in this room. They were then guided through the vault which displayed local jewellery and on to the Grog Shoppe.

The royal couple was next escorted to the elegant courtyard at the back of Devon House to visit the craft shops. They were very interested in the works demonstrating the different stages of weaving and the baking of bread in the ancient ovens. During the tour the Mystic Revelation of Rastafari played.

At the end of the tour Mr Seaga's youngest son, Andrew, presented the Queen with a present for her grandson, Prince William, on behalf of the children of Jamaica. The gift of a Jamaican quilt had been specially designed and made by Susan Casebeer of Things Jamaican. On a background of blue, orange and yellow there were a series of white egrets. Annabella Seaga also stepped forward to present the Queen with a bouquet of flowers.

On the east lawns of the house near to the verandah, a marquee had been set up for the tables of food. The royal couple headed the queue with scores of invited guests, and enjoyed a choice of such dishes as steamship round of beef, béarnaise sauce, chicken, Boston jerk pork, ackee and salt fish, jacket potatoes, mixed cole slaw, assorted breads, coconut cream pie, banana cream pie, potato pone, mango ice-cream, fresh fruit salad and Blue Mountain coffee. Sheltered from view by the potted palms, the Queen enjoyed her meal in safety.

CHAPTER 7
Devon House Today

M r Seaga recalls when the government bought Devon House in 1968: 'I did not know what to do with the house. The idea came to me in a flash, a place to display Jamaican art and craft, also Jamaican food and drink and open the house to visitors. I spoke to the then Director of Tourism, John Pringle, and he was very keen on the concept!'

Later when Mr Seaga was Prime Minister of Jamaica, he knew that with a government traditionally short of money it was essential to make Devon House self-supporting, so in 1987 with a grant from the European Economic Community, he planned to increase the commercial potential of the property. By this time Jamaicans had taken Devon House to their hearts and had a personal pride in the lovely old house. When the work on these commercial improvements started many Jamaicans objected. They were horror-stricken at the suggestion that the house was to be commercialized, as they wanted it preserved in its unspoilt beauty.

Trenches were dug for the laying of pipes, and gangs of workers turned the gardens into a dust bowl. Mounds of earth grew and scaffolding started to rise around the house. The last straw was when zinc fences were erected. Then letters from people like Sonia Jones, Attorney-at-Law, came flooding into the *Daily Gleaner*. Articles appeared daily, and for weeks a furore raged. The objectors were determined to stop what they considered the desecration of

Devon House. Across the island the chief topic of conversation was the Devon House controversy.

The cautious withheld their criticism until they could see the end result. When Mr Seaga said that he could name a flavour of the Devon House ice cream 'eat your words', this infuriated the critics even more. With no abatement in the flood of objecting letters, Mr Seaga hastened to Devon House. When he saw the aviary which was being erected he ordered it to be demolished immediately as he thought it a monstrosity. Mr Seaga himself had for long taken a keen interest in Devon House, and far from wanting to build anything to detract from its beauty, he wanted buildings erected that were in keeping with its character and the period.

In spite of the persistent criticism, in 1990 Devon House was the recipient of the American Express Historic Preservation Award. Tom Concannon would have been pleased to know that his restoration work on Devon House had been honoured. In 1972 Devon House had also been honoured by being chosen to be depicted on a Puerto Rican nine cent stamp. It was also featured in an article in the *Caribbean Week* (Nov 10–16) by Larry Luxner entitled *Preserving Its Usefulness*. In it he writes, 'Restoration of Jamaica's Devon House turns into a thriving commercial concern.'

Today, with tempers cooled, critics have to admit that the end result of these commercial improvements is not only a success, but was accomplished in mostly such good taste that the structures meld happily with the old house. Before 1987 the garden boasted few flowers, and the lawns that led to the fence were flat so that the Abbey Court Apartments hit you in the eye as you stepped out of the house. Today the landscape gardeners have created rolling lawns which rise steeply towards the south fence, and on top of these heights they have planted trees which now hide much of the Abbey Court Apartments from view and make the gardens infinitely more private.

The new addition of the bandstand on the west shelters the band from rain and sun, and often a band plays on a Sunday to the enjoyment of visitors. As we walk down the winding pathway under a giant age-old tree around which cluster flowering shrubs, we come to a pond over which there is a picturesque bridge. Below, ducks sail and frolic in the water and school children lean over the rails to admire a sight which city-bred children hardly ever see. Returning, we pass by the 'I Scream' kiosks, busy with customers whose favourite ice creams are flavoured with Jamaican fruit such as mango and guava. Commenting on the strange spelling of this shop, Mr Seaga said, 'When I was about nine my father took me to have an ice cream; as he handed me the cone he said, "You scream, I scream," so that's the name I gave it.'

As we walk towards the west side of the house we come to the lately-built restaurant discreetly tucked away behind trees and flowering shrubs. It was built with the same rose coloured bricks that Tom Concannon used in his earlier restoration. The only offending sight is the portico which is not in keeping with the period of the nineteenth-century mansion. As we mount the steps we are greeted with tinkling water falling from fountains, and

Edward Seaga. He 'saved' Devon House from the Developers. Responsible for Devon House's modern development.

"You Scream I Scream".

The Devonshire: Up-market dining at Devon House, with its anachronistic portico.

artistically arranged shrubs and ferns hang over the artificial pools in which gold fish swim. Over an ornamental bridge we cross the pools to an open-sided room where cocktail parties are often held, and in front to the north is the popular 'up-market' dining room called the Devonshire Gourmet Restaurant.

As we enter the Grog Shoppe's courtyard we are met with the happy laughter and chatter of young people who congregate in and around the old coach house. This was used by the seventeenth century rectors to house the carriages and later as a garage for the last private owner, Cecil Lindo. Mr Seaga explained that he had heard that teenagers were going to undesirable places and so he opened the Grog Shoppe on the line of an English pub especially for teenagers, so they could meet and enjoy music and reasonable food and drink in pleasant surroundings.

Grog Shoppe Terrace Restaurant.

Certainly, when we walk through to the rear courtyard there is a sense of regret that the clean lines of the original courtyard have been cluttered with skeleton structures, but thankfully they will one day be draped in flowering creepers and we have to admit that they do serve a useful purpose as here the ice cream customers can sit while they enjoy the delicious ice cream. The important fact is that Devon House is now on its way to being self-supporting with its ten craft shops, three restaurants, bakery, ice cream kiosks and flower pavilions. And with all these alterations the beauty of the old house has not been impaired.

At the opening of these additions a cocktail party was given at which guests wandered through the gardens enjoying delicious lobster patties and ice cream. Mr Seaga and his sister, Mrs Hugh Hart, were most interested and active in the promotion of Devon House. Reminding us that the house was once George Stiebel's beloved family home, his great grandson Dickie Jackson and his vivacious wife Gladys attended the function.

Today business people and visitors meet on the verandah for a light lunch; there are weddings galore; students study in the shady nooks of the gardens; grandmothers celebrate their birthdays; and the time-old coach house is a well sought after meeting place for the young. How proud George Stiebel would have been to know that his Devon House had been awarded the American Express 1990 Historic Preservation Award, and happier still he would have been to know that his grandson Arthur's widow, Nora, had celebrated her ninetieth birthday at Devon House, where as a young girl she had been married. Her daughters, Audrey and Bunny, and their children and husbands flew down from Canada to be with her. Dickie and Jennifer with their children were also there. One and all had inherited the charm of their great grandfather.

As they clustered around Nora, 'Nanoon' as they called her, it was clear to see that she was an adored mother and grandmother. On her ninetieth birthday she looked superb; tall and straight she stood in a long black dress with ropes of long pearls about her neck. She is a wonderful lady at ninety; she not only crochets tablecloths for her children, but she also makes all the family Christmas puddings. An amazing woman, she keeps abreast of world affairs and moves with the times, although she often laughs at the things to which she has had to adjust.

Although George Stiebel could not be there in person, we are sure he was there in spirit, glowing with pride to see his descendants and his well-loved Devon House. How proud he would have been to know what part his 'dream house' plays in Jamaica today, and that it was declared a National Monument.

APPENDICES

Author's Acknowledgements

I gratefully acknowledge the help of all those who gave me information especially, Nora Jackson, Richard Jackson, Gordon Miller, Bunny Wriggles, the late Dorothy Gayson, Rosemary Von Witt, Rita Landale, Margaret Genis, Philip Yawman, Sergio Dello Strologo, Louise White, Sir John Golding, Neville Alexander, Lucille Bubb-Clarke, Sybil Bradbury, Oliver Cox, Barbara Cargill, Herbert Hart, Ann Hodges and Rodney Smedmore.

I also thank the staff who helped me at the Jamaica Archives, the National Library of Jamaica and the Records Office, Spanish Town.

Marguerite Curtin made helpful suggestions at an early stage of the writing and Karen Brown read the final typescript for typographical errors and assisted with reading the proofs.

Special thanks go to Glory Robertson of the Jamaica Historical Society who edited the manuscript throughout.

Publisher's Acknowledgements

The Publishers wish to thank the Board of Things Jamaican Limited and the management and staff of Devon House for their cooperation in and support for this venture. We also acknowledge the assistance of Ray McIntyre of APEC Ltd, and the staff of the Jamaica Information Service, the Gleaner Company and the National Library of Jamaica.

We also thank Mr Alty Benjamin and Mr Llewellyn Brown for supplying photographs for the text. Front cover photo – courtesy Ray Chen. Back cover photo – courtesy Alty Benjamin. Line drawing of Devon House by Anghelen Arrington Philips on the title page is reproduced with the kind permission of the publishers of *Jamaican Houses a Vanishing Legacy*.

Rectors of St Andrew Parish Church

James Zellers 1644–1700
John Moodie 1700–1710
George Wright 1710–1714
John Cary 1714–1738
Alexander Inglis 1738–1747
George Eccles 1747–1760
Gideon Castlefranc 1760–1768
John Poole LLB 1768–1782
John Campbell MA 1782–1813
Alexander Campbell MA 1813–1858
Richard Parton DD 1858–1860
William Mayhew MA 1861–1870
George Taylor Braine BA 1870–1872
Alexander Duncan
    Campbell 1872–1878
Hubert Headlam Isaacs MA
    1879–1900

Chronology

1667 Charles II granted the glebe lands, including Devon Penn, to Rev. Mr John Zellers.

1750 Devon Penn rectory built.

1787 Extensive repairs made to Devon Penn rectory.

1782–1878 The Campbell families occupied Devon Penn rectory except for a period of twenty-four years.

1879 'The lay body of the church' sold Devon Penn to George Stiebel.

1881 George Stiebel built Devon House.

1896 George Stiebel died. His daughter Theresa Stiebel Jackson owned Devon House.

1922 Theresa Stiebel Jackson died.

1923 Reginald Melhado bought Devon House.

1928 Cecil Lindo bought Devon House for his wife Agnes Irene.

1967 The National Trust bought Devon House. Restoration by Tom Concannon started.

1968 The Hon. Edward Seaga opened the Grog Shoppe.

1973 The Prime Minister, the Hon. Michael Manley made Devon House the National Gallery.

1980 The Prime Minister, the Hon. Edward Seaga had Devon House furnished on the lines of a nineteenth century great house.

1983 Her Majesty Queen Elizabeth II visited Devon House.

FAMILY TREES

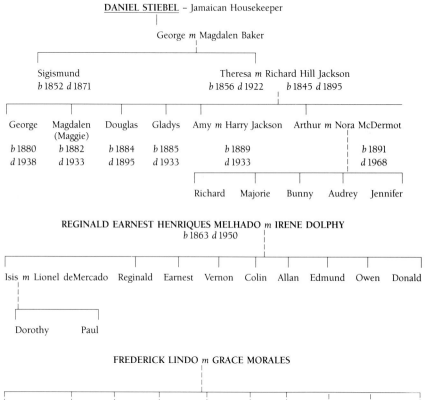

DANIEL STIEBEL – Jamaican Housekeeper

George *m* Magdalen Baker

Sigismund
b 1852 *d* 1871

Theresa *m* Richard Hill Jackson
b 1856 *d* 1922   *b* 1845 *d* 1895

George
b 1880
d 1938

Magdalen
(Maggie)
b 1882
d 1933

Douglas
b 1884
d 1895

Gladys
b 1885
d 1933

Amy *m* Harry Jackson
b 1889
d 1933

Arthur *m* Nora McDermot
b 1891
d 1968

Richard   Majorie   Bunny   Audrey   Jennifer

REGINALD EARNEST HENRIQUES MELHADO *m* **IRENE DOLPHY**
b 1863 *d* 1950

Isis *m* Lionel deMercado   Reginald   Earnest   Vernon   Colin   Allan   Edmund   Owen   Donald

Dorothy   Paul

FREDERICK LINDO *m* **GRACE MORALES**

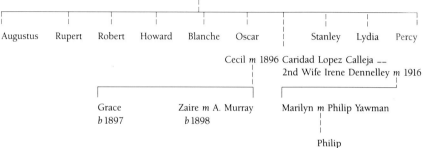

Augustus   Rupert   Robert   Howard   Blanche   Oscar   Stanley   Lydia   Percy

Cecil *m* 1896 Caridad Lopez Calleja __
2nd Wife Irene Dennelley *m* 1916

Grace
b 1897

Zaire *m* A. Murray
b 1898

Marilyn *m* Philip Yawman

Philip

HOUSE FLOOR PLANS

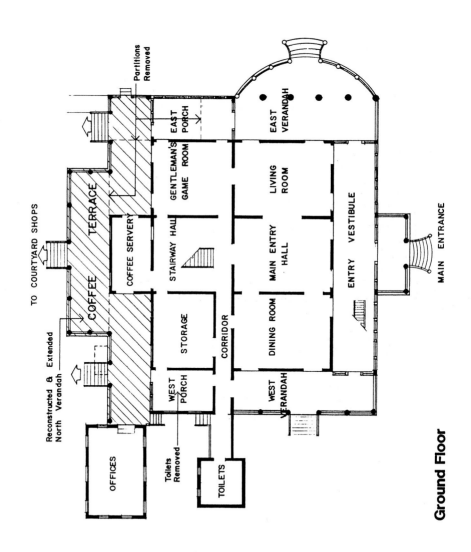

Ground Floor

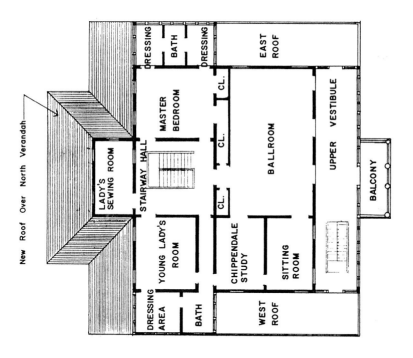

New Roof Over North Verandah

DRESSING

BATH

DRESSING

EAST ROOF

LADY'S SEWING ROOM

STAIRWAY HALL

MASTER BEDROOM

CL.

CL.

UPPER VESTIBULE

BALLROOM

BALCONY

DRESSING AREA

BATH

YOUNG LADY'S ROOM

CL.

CHIPPENDALE STUDY

SITTING ROOM

WEST ROOF

Upper Floor

GROUND PLANS

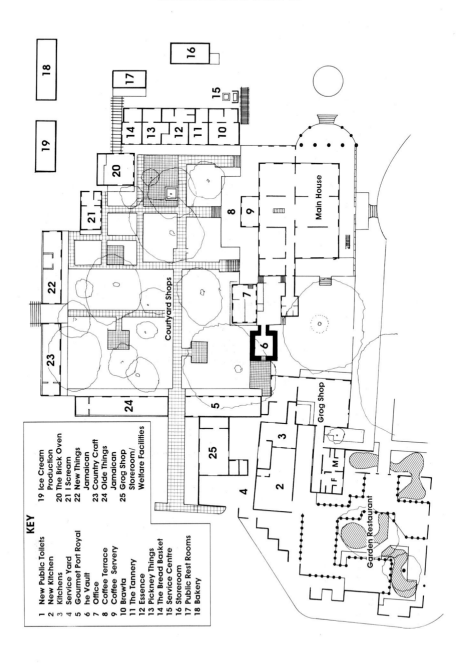

KEY

1 New Public Toilets
2 New Kitchen
3 Kitchens
4 Service Yard
5 Gourmet Port Royal
6 The Vault
7 Office
8 Coffee Terrace
9 Coffee Servery
10 Brawta
11 The Tannery
12 Essence
13 Pickney Things
14 The Bread Basket
15 Service Centre
16 Storeroom
17 Public Rest Rooms
18 Bakery
19 Ice Cream Production
20 The Brick Oven
21 I Scream
22 New Things Jamaican
23 Country Craft
24 Olde Things Jamaican
25 Grog Shop Storeroom/ Welfare Facilities

Main House

Courtyard Shops

Grog Shop

Garden Restaurant

DEVELOPMENT PLANS

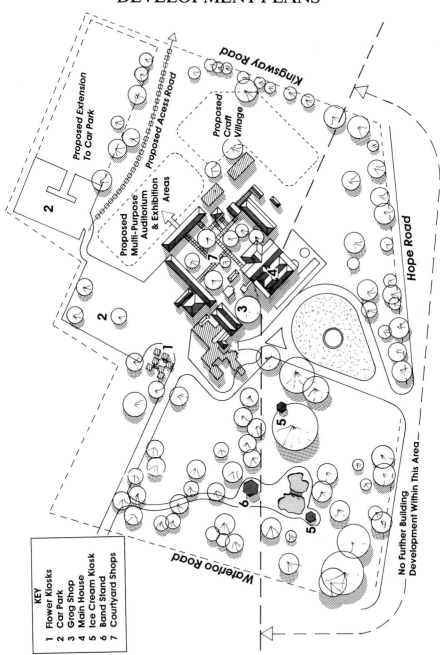

Kingsway Road

Proposed Extension
To Car Park

Proposed Aces Road

Proposed
Craft
Village

Proposed
Multi-Purpose
Auditorium
& Exhibition
Areas

Hope Road

Waterloo Road

No Further Building
Development Within This Area

KEY
1 Flower Kiosks
2 Car Park
3 Grog Shop
4 Main House
5 Ice Cream Kiosk
6 Band Stand
7 Courtyard Shops

BIBLIOGRAPHY

Black, Clinton. *History of Jamaica*. Collins, London and Glasgow, 1958.

Black, Clinton. *The Story of Jamaica*. Collins, London, 1865.

Cundall, Frank. *Parish Church of St Andrew*. Institute of Jamaica, 1931.

Daily Gleaner. *Geography and History of Jamaica*. Revised, 1973.

Daily Gleaner. 'Death of George Stiebel'. 30 June 1896.

Daily Gleaner. Report on George Stiebel's furneral. 18 July 1896.

Daily Gleaner. Advertisement auction of Devon House furniture. 12 February 1923.

Daily Gleaner. Obituary to Reginald Melhado. 15 February 1950.

Daily Gleaner. Report on opening of Devon House shops. 24 January 1968.

Daily Gleaner. Thomas Wright's article on Devon House. 11 May 1971.

Daily Gleaner. Report on the Queen's visit to Devon House. 18 February 1983.

Daily Gleaner. Sunday Magazine, article on National Gallery. 15 March 1981.

Diocese of Jamaica. *Tercentenary Year 1664-1964.*

Evans, E. L. *A History of the Diocese of Jamaica*. The Society for the Promotion of Christian Knowledge, 1913.

Gall's Weekly News Letter. Description of the funeral of Richard Hill Jackson. 27 June 1895.

Jamaica Archives, Spanish Town. Vestry Minutes of the Parish Church of St Andrew. Naturalization Records of Stiebel, 1823. Patent to Zellers, 1667, Vol. 12, Folio 148. Lindo's Private Journal 4/70/1/1.

Jamaica Post. Death of George Stiebel. 1 July 1896.

Lambeth Palace Archives, London. Letters to the Bishop of London from the clergy in Jamaica.

Munchie, Anita Gregoria. *Imported Spices:A Study of Anglo American Settlers in Costa Rica 1821-1900*. Ministry of Culture and Sports, Department of Publications, San José, Costa Rica, 1981.

National Library of Jamaica, Kingston. Files on George Stiebel, Jackson, Cecil Lindo, Reginald Melhado, Devon House.

Planters Punch. 1925-26. 'Initiative, Industry, Success', pp. 18-20.

Planters Punch. 1929. 'The Dream and the Busienss', p. 18.

Planters Punch. 1936-37. 'A Fraternity of Success', p. 26.

Planters PLunch. 1939-40. 'From Herring to Beef', pp. 13-14.

Registrar General's Department, Spanish Town. Wills of Alexander Campbell, George Stiebel, Irene Melhado, Cecil Lindon. Deeds, 'Lay body of the Church of England' to George Stiebel, 1878, 1881.

Registrar of Titles Office, Kingson. Stiebel and Melhado, Vol. 216, Folio 76.

Sealy, Theodore and Herbert Hart. *Jamaica's Banana Industry*. The Jamaica Banana Producers' Association, Kingston, 1984.

Strologo, Sergio Dello 'Devon House.' *Jamaica Journal*, Vol. 17, No. 2, May 1984, pp. 33-40.

Who's Who 1930-40, Kingston.

Wray & Nephew Ltd., Kingston. Files on Cecil Lindo. 'The Story of the Lindo Brothers'.

To. Imelda -   - 2006 -
From :- Jennifer & Mike .